GEORGE
DAWSON
the
little
giant

GEORGE DAWSON
the
little
giant

Joyce C. Barkhouse

CLARKE, IRWIN & COMPANY LIMITED/ TORONTO/ VANCOUVER

© 1974 by Clarke, Irwin & Company Limited

ISBN 0-7720-0734 9

1 2 3 4 5 6/79 78 77 76 75 74

Published simultaneously in the United States by
    Books Canada Inc., 33 East Tupper Street, Buffalo, N.Y. 14203,
and in the United Kingdom by
    Books Canada Limited, 17 Cockspur Street, Suite 600, London SW1Y 5BP.

Printed in Canada

1164

For
Kathleen and Kari
Alexandra and Ian

This book could not have been written without
the kind help of George Dawson's niece
Lois Winslow-Spragge.
I am also grateful to Mrs. Winslow-Spragge
for her generosity in providing the photographs
and illustrations.

Contents

Foreword

George Dawson was one of the most popular and admired men of his day. A geologist who was appointed Director of the Geological Survey of Canada in 1895, he was a brilliant man whose contribution to Canadian knowledge was enormous. But it was neither of these qualities that made him popular and admired. It was his courage.

"He was a l'il hunchback runt—couldn't be more'n four foot eight or ten," said an old miner who knew him. "When he was in camp he was first up in the mornin' and off over the hills like a he-goat. Wasn't none of us could keep up with him. Be dark when he got back to camp. An' I don't think he never got no decent sleep. Suffered something cruel from that back of his'n."

George was born in 1849 in Pictou, Nova Scotia, the son of Sir William Dawson, who is known as the father of McGill University. It was evident from his early childhood that George had a bright and enquiring mind, and it was expected that he would become an academic man. At the age of ten, however, he was crippled by illness, and then his parents assumed he would spend his life at home working as assistant to his father. But shelter and a quiet life were not for George. He made his way on his own, with his own talents and his own great courage.

When he died at the age of fifty-two George Dawson was not only Director of the Geological Survey of Canada, he had been created a Companion of the Order of St. Michael and St. George by Queen Victoria, was President of the Geological Society of America, and the holder of uncounted scientific honours. He had made some of the most epic exploratory journeys in the history of Canada. He was the first educated man to explore and map the Yukon, and Dawson City is named in his honour.

Men who worked with Dawson on his expeditions sometimes said that he had a body—and a heart—of steel. Possessed of boundless enthusiasm, he seemed never to hunger or tire. He could work all day on a tin of beans and a handful of berries—and expected others to do the same.

"Physical weakness and disease never repressed his bright spirits. His constant cheerfulness was a source of surprise to everyone who knew him, more especially those who reflected upon the fortitude required to bear his infirmities with patience. In conversation he was witty and humorous to a degree." That was how a contemporary saw him.

The Indians called him Skookum Tumtum, brave cheery man. They shared their legends with him and taught him their languages.

In the world of cities and universities he was in great demand as a public speaker. His expeditions were fascinating. He was a first-rate lecturer and had the unusual knack of explaining scientific material in clear, simple language easily understood by anyone.

The story of George Dawson's life is important to Canadian history and to everyone who admires courage.

JOYCE C. BARKHOUSE

Kinsman's Corners
June 1974

1
Disaster

School was out. George Dawson slung his book-strap over his shoulder and tried to walk steadily toward the wooden sidewalk. Once he stumbled and almost fell.

"Hey, Dawson! What are we doing today?"

"Going on another rock collecting expedition?"

"Can I be on your team, Dawson?"

Five boys pushed around him. George pulled a red woollen cap down over his ears. The April wind felt cold on his hot face. He shivered.

"It's a great day to play Shoot the Rapids. The brook is flooded—like a river," he said. He hoped his voice sounded natural.

"Yes, let's play Fur Traders again! Voyageurs against the Bay!" shouted Dan O'Hara. He was a skinny boy with straight black eyebrows and was George's best friend.

"Let's go!"

They raced off along the cobblestoned streets up the steep hill toward McGill College where George's father was Principal. In the year 1861 the few unfinished buildings of the small college at the foot of Mount Royal in Montreal were still surrounded by rough pastureland. It lay so far outside the city that George had never attended a regular school until now, when he was almost eleven years old. Except for his younger sister, Anna, and his two little brothers, William and Rankine, he had hardly ever played with other children. He had been taught at home, under a series of governesses, and as a result, the first months at Montreal High School had been tough. He had had to suffer all the taunts and insults that a new boy must endure, especially if he is different in any way.

George was different. He was small—the smallest in the class—and strong. His broad, high forehead and his extraordinarily bright eyes told the world clearly that he meant to be a leader, which won him the respect and envy of his classmates. He spoke with the Scottish accent of his mother and father and he used the big words and bookish expressions his years of secluded schooling had taught him. This made some of the boys laugh scornfully and caused the headmaster's thin, stern mouth to twitch with amusement.

By nature George was not only determined to take charge, he was good tempered and full of fun. His years of genteel governesses hadn't in the least put down his high spirits. When the boys teased him, he usually grinned and shrugged; but he could become coldly angry. Then his blue eyes turned to ice and somehow that stopped a bully quicker than a punch to the jaw. It wasn't long before he was joining in every sport; but as soon as the bell rang for classes, his character seemed to change. He really loved learning things and was absolutely serious about his studies. He was deaf and blind to all temptations to play pranks in school. Before many months had passed he was making top marks. A few of the boys grew jealous and spiteful, but between the beginning of the term in September and that day in April when he and his friends ran up the slope of Mount Royal, he had become one of the most popular boys at the school.

He invented and led in most of the games they played. Playing Fur Traders, George's version of what was happening at that time in the Canadian Northwest, had been their favourite sport for most of the winter, and George had been their accepted leader.

He didn't want them to know he felt so ill.

"If I can just hang on a little longer, maybe it'll disappear," he thought.

Lately he had been having a series of headaches, and today his head was bursting with pain. Every once in a while it seemed as if the high scream of a sawmill was ripping through his brain. Still he kept on running.

When they reached the brook he led the way to a clump of alder bushes, where he had hidden some miniature canoes he had spent a week building out of birchbark.

"Hey, Dawson, these are jolly good!" exclaimed a newcomer.

"Are you going to be on the Bay team? I want to be on your side, Dawson," O'Hara announced.

"That's not fair. You were on his side last time," protested a rosy-cheeked boy named Craig.

"Craig and Smith should be the leaders. They've never had a turn before," said George.

He broke two twigs from an alder bush, and hid them

behind his back.

"Choose, Craig," he said. "The long one is for Hudson's Bay, and the short one for Voyageurs."

In a few minutes the boys had chosen sides. It turned out that O'Hara and Dawson were Voyageurs. But now another squabble started.

"Craig's got the best canoe. Mine's lop-sided. Look, she tips when you put 'er in the water."

George gritted his teeth and shivered. He wished they'd start the race and get it over. He couldn't stand the pain much longer. If only the sun would come out from behind the dark clouds or if the wind would stop blowing . . . .

"We'll have to number the canoes. Anybody got a pencil? Here's a bit of paper. We'll put numbers in my cap. The number each fellow pulls out, that's the number of his canoe," he directed patiently.

"Fair enough," agreed Smith.

After the canoes were allotted, more time was spent in selecting small stones for ballast, and then for cutting long poles which were needed to guide the boats on their way through the swift currents.

"What if one capsizes?"

"It doesn't matter, Whichever side gets all its canoes to the fort first—that's at the footbridge—that side wins."

"My Papa'll kill me if I get my feet wet again," muttered Smith, just as George stepped into an icy puddle that oozed over the tops of his boots.

The race was on. Away went the tiny canoes, bobbing and dancing this way and that in the swirling waters. To the boys the brook had become a great Canadian river, and each boat bore a cargo of furs—beaver, marten, fox, wolverine, mink and muskrat. Spring was the time for traders to carry their precious cargo south, and the first men to arrive could bargain for the highest prices.

"Look out! Come on, Dawson!" shouted O'Hara.

But George stood uncertainly where he was, trying to steady himself with his pole. A robin, perched on the twig of a willow tree, seemed to sway dizzily, then the whole earth began to spin. Suddenly the pain in his head burst like a bubble. The blood drained from his face and he toppled forward into the brook.

Impatiently O'Hara turned to see why George was not coming. For a moment he was too astonished to move. Then he screamed, "Help!" at the top of his lungs and ran to the rescue.

Between them, the boys pulled George out of the water, but they couldn't bring him to.

"He's dead."

"No, he's not! He can't be!" cried O'Hara, looking around desperately. "You stay with him. I'll get his father."

In minutes that seemed hours, George's father came running to the scene. Five other professors, their black academic gowns flapping in the wind, were right behind. The boys hovered about in awed silence, watching, while the men wrapped George's small, stiff body in a blanket and carried him home.

There were no telephones in Montreal in 1861, and the boys did not know until they went to school the next day that their friend was not dead. He was desperately ill.

In the east wing of the McGill College building where the

Dawsons lived, the sick boy burned with fever. His head, lying rigid on his pillow, ached violently, and he had nightmares. George had often had frightening dreams before but never anything so terrible and vivid as those that came to haunt his sick bed now. As a small child he had thought that dreams came floating in through windows and that when Mamma or his governess pulled down blinds they were shutting out dreams. He had never liked this, because he wasn't afraid of the dark or the out-of-doors, and dreams were such strange and curious adventures.

Nightmares were different. In wild desperation he felt himself caught in hopeless situations, struggling against suffocation and death.

He was an explorer somewhere in Canada's Far North and he was trying to guide his canoe through treacherous rapids. He grasped the paddle with all his strength, but the craft turned sideways. It hit a rock, it overturned, cold water swirled over his head. He was drowning.

He moaned aloud and gasped for breath.

"Shh. Shh."

A nurse in a long starched white cotton apron sat beside his bed, but George did not know she was there. His blue eyes stared at her blankly, then closed. He began to dream again.

He was in a deep cave following a path that led steeply down into the depths of the earth. In his hand was a flaming torch. Strange, flickering shadows danced all around. Now a shaft of bright light slanted down and he saw that the walls of the cave were formed of neat layers of rock, like a diagram in a geological textbook. To his astonishment he

6

could read the layers and he muttered the names:
"Cambrian, Ordovician, Silurian."

"Shh. Shh," said the nurse again. She thought the words
were gibberish. It was night and she held a lighted candle
in her hand as she bent over her patient. George could not
move his head, and his eyes flinched from the light. He
had always wanted to be a geologist, and he knew the
meanings of the words he was muttering.

*Instead of a torch, he thought he held a hammer and he
pounded at the walls of the cave. The vibrations hurt his
head. He was looking for fossils. A slab of rock came away.
A rich find! The slab was encrusted with trilobites, but
when he examined the bug-like markings more closely he
saw that they were not made of stone. They were alive,
they were running away! The cave was full of strange,
many-legged creatures. They were crawling all over him.*

"Help! Help! Grandpa!" he cried; and his small hands
fluttered helplessly over the bright patchwork quilt. His
mother entered the darkened room with a soft rustle of
long silk skirts trailing across the floor.

"He's calling for his grandfather," whispered the nurse.

"Yes, I know, we've sent a message to Nova Scotia. His
grandpa's coming."

Margaret Dawson't delicate oval face was white under
her dark hair.

"I've come to relieve you. The children are having tea in
the study. Would you care to join them?" she asked softly.

The nurse tiptoed away, and Mrs. Dawson leaned forward to stroke her son's feverish forehead gently. Under
the soothing touch his breathing became more even, and

7

he lay quiet. His mother sank back in the chair, exhausted with worry.

Very little was known about the diseases of the human body in the middle of the last century. Nothing was known about germs or viruses. There were no X-rays, no wonder drugs; and even many common diseases were as yet unidentified and unnamed. Physicians of today, looking at photographs of George, and reading about his symptoms, say that, although no one could put a name to it then, perhaps he suffered from polio.

In the days and weeks that followed George's collapse by the brook his father tried desperately to save the life of his oldest son. The best Montreal doctors were consulted, but none of their prescriptions helped. The boy lay paralyzed. No treatment eased his raging headache. Urgent messages were sent to Boston—then the centre of the medical world in North America—and prominent specialists made the long journey to George's bedside. These learned men shook their heads gravely. They could not diagnose the disease and they knew of no cure. They agreed only that the boy must have caught a severe chill which had in some way affected and injured his spine. They told his heart-broken parents that the boy would probably not recover; or, if he lived, would be paralyzed for life.

But the doctors were wrong. George lived, and he learned to walk again; but sometime during the weeks of his severe illness and the months and years of convalescence which followed he had to face an awful truth: a day came when he finally realized that his younger sister, Anna, and even his little brothers, William and Rankine, would always tower head and shoulders above him.

He had stopped growing. His shoulders were pulled forward, and his back was deformed. The handsome, healthy boy had been transformed into a tiny hunchback.

2
Family

George had been born in 1849 in the seaport town of Pictou, Nova Scotia, and lived there until he was six. He was
the second child of William and Margaret (Mercer) Dawson.
An older brother had died in infancy, and Anna, a year
younger than George, was his only playmate. The fourth
child, William, was still a baby when the family moved to
Montreal.

In Pictou, the Dawson family lived with George's grand-
parents. His grandfather, James Dawson, a tall, grave Scots-
man who had emigrated as a young man, preserved strict
discipline in the Presbyterian home where his sad-faced wife
ruled in the kitchen. Grandma Dawson wore long black
skirts and a tiny black bonnet pinned to her thin grey hair.
It seemed to George that she was always crying into a damp
lace handkerchief, and she died when he was only five years
old. After that, home seemed a happier place, for his own
mother was cheerful and bustling and full of energy and affection. Often she sang and laughed when she was alone
with her children and the young servant girls, though she
was instantly prim and proper when Grandpa came home.

George and Anna were not permitted to roam the streets, frequented by rough and drunken sailors, or to play with other children who might be considered to have a bad influence. The Dawsons kept to themselves. From the grassy yard of their home on the hill the children could watch tall vessels come sailing into the harbour from far places to discharge their cargoes and load up again with sweet-smelling timbers from the forests of Nova Scotia, or with rank bales of dried codfish. As he watched the great windjammers spread their sails and head out of Northumberland Strait toward the grey waters of the North Atlantic, George dreamed that one day he himself would get aboard just such a graceful ship, and travel all around the world—if he had time, after he had finished exploring Canada.

George would have been a very lonely boy if it had not been for Anna. Anna was a well-behaved child, and dutifully performed all the domestic chores that were required of small females in the Victorian era. In the time she had to herself she sometimes played with baby William and rocked him in his cradle, but she worshipped George. Even as a toddler she tried to imitate him and join in his inventions, plans and projects. In most of them Anna was the appreciative audience but when it came to drawing and painting she excelled. George's pictures were usually funnier but Anna's artistic ability was superior to his, as George always admitted.

His only other friend at that time was his grandfather. Because his father, then Superintendent of Education for Nova Scotia, was away from home for months each year, George spent a lot of time with his grandfather. Sometimes

11

they went on walks in the pastures and woodlands which surrounded the town, looking for fossils and plants and wildlife. Sometimes George went with him to his places of business. Grandpa owned a printing shop and a general store and also some sailing ships which traded in the West Indies. He loved to tell stories, and George and Anna listened spellbound to the tales of Grandpa's boyhood in Scotland and the long adventures of his youth, as they sat at his knee beside the cosy fireplace.

"I was the youngest but one of ten children, born in Overtown in Banffshire," Grandpa always began his story. "My father was a farmer, a powerful man who stood six foot three in his socks. One of my brothers, George, went to university, and I wanted to go, too, but a severe attack of smallpox in childhood left me with weak eyes."

Pictou from Fort Hill—a drawing by Wm. Eagar

(George and Anna knew that well enough; they were always hunting for Grandpa's glasses.) Then Grandpa would add,

"I pray that you, too, will go to university, like your namesake, George. For my part, I went to a church school and laboured on the farm with my father until I was seventeen, when I begged to be apprenticed. I became a saddler, a craftsman in leather. In 1811, at the age of twenty-two, I came to Nova Scotia."

Grandpa always stopped at this point and rocked back and forth with his head bowed, his big hands folded under his flowing white beard, and George knew he was thinking about his family he had left behind in Scotland. The children waited respectfully, not daring to urge Grandpa to go on, and tell how he and his three friends had walked 180

miles across Scotland from Banffshire to Greenock to board ship for Nova Scotia in the bitter cold of early spring. The part of this story George liked best was the day that the young men came to a great cave in the side of a mountain and saw farmers, with oxen and carts, digging out soil and using it as fertilizer.

"Upon examining this soil, we found it to consist of millions of tiny shells," said Grandpa, as he continued his story. "We were filled with amazement. How could a mountain, so far from the sea, be composed entirely of shells?"

Here George and Anna giggled, because their Papa was a geologist—and he often told them, the way some fathers tell nursery rhymes—about the great upheavals of earth and sea and the wonderful changes which had taken place since the beginning of time. At this place in the story Grandpa always took his good luck piece out of his pocket.

"It was near that cave that I found the stone. It's called a cairngorm," said Grandpa, and he held up a sparkling bit of quartz. George would take it in his hands. He liked the feel of the rock and to watch how the golden brown prisms sparkled as he turned it in the firelight.

"It was through prayer, and hard work, and by using my brains," said the old man, "that I devised ways of making money in my spare time in the evenings, even while I worked full time as a saddler. For one thing, I bought up furs from Indians and trappers, and made them into caps for boys and men."

"And into muffs and tippets for ladies," said Anna.

Grandpa patted Anna's neat brown curls.

"You must always save your money, as I did. I never

14

wasted my earnings by frequenting taverns, or indulging in idle sports. In this way, by the grace of God, I was soon able to buy my first sailing ship, and within twelve years from the time of my arrival here, I owned a dozen such traders, I was then one of the richest men in Pictou, and then God saw fit to punish me."

God was the biggest part of Grandpa's teaching of the Dawson children. His failures and later successes in business were all in God's plans. Walks in the woods, talks in the shipyard, reminiscences all centred around the will and meaning of God, and many a meal grew cold upon the table while Grandpa prayed long and fervently for God's continued blessing.

In spite of the lectures and long prayers George loved and respected his grandfather, but his hero-worship was reserved for his father. He was beside himself with excitement on those occasions when William Dawson arrived home from one of his long trips. Usually he came by steamer, and George watched and waited wistfully for a trail of black smoke in the sky which foretold the arrival of one of those dirty, smelly, noisy passenger boats at the wharf. Sometimes his father came by stagecoach from Halifax, weary and bruised from bumping over miles of rough, muddy roads, but invariably cheerful and good-natured. He swept his children up in his strong arms for welcoming hugs and kisses, and in the days that followed, no matter how busy he was—and he was an unbelievably busy man—he always had time for his children. With infinite patience he would answer George's myriad questions; the little boy had an insatiable curiosity.

When George was a year old, his father had become the first Superintendent of Education for Nova Scotia, and for the next five years he travelled all over the colony. On horseback, by boat, by stagecoach, by horse and buggy, and even on foot, he visited every school district, collecting information for a report on conditions in the public schools.

Hundreds of the early settlers could neither read nor write, and they didn't care whether their children did, either. There was no compulsory education, no training for teachers, and in many of the drafty one-room schools the children had no books. George's father made changes that gave Nova Scotia's children a much better system of education.

William Dawson had come upon the study of geology as a little boy. He had been digging for soft rock behind the schoolhouse for slate pencils. A flake of stone had split and the perfect shape of a fern-like leaf had been exposed. He'd been astonished and so curious that he'd found the courage to take his find to Thomas McCulloch, the Principal of Pictou Academy. Dr. McCulloch had told him about fossils and the study of geology and, from that moment William Dawson had been, heart and soul, a geologist. He became well known as a scientist, a pioneer in many fields, before he became an educator. He was one of the first to understand how coal is formed. At the age of twenty-two he had established a museum at Pictou to demonstrate that the coal beds of Nova Scotia were of three distinct types, not all the same, as had previously been supposed. And when Sir Charles Lyell, a prominent British geologist, had visited Nova Scotia around that time, he had

16

been astounded by the young man's wide knowledge and original ideas.

Everywhere Dawson went he carried a geologist's hammer, and when he returned to Pictou he brought with him boxes of rocks and shells and fossils which made George jump for joy, for he was always more interested in shells and trilobites than he was in toys.

William recognized that his eldest son was an exceptional child. "George will go far," he told his wife one evening after the children had been tucked into bed. "He has an inquiring mind, the memory of an elephant, and already you can see he's a perfectionist. He'll grow up to be a great scientist."

Margaret smiled. "A scientist? I'm not so sure. I think he's more likely to be a great humorist. Yesterday he put a toad in Annie Archer's bedroom. What a scene! I couldn't convince George it wasn't funny to frighten the poor maid. He kept insisting, between spasms of laughter, 'But it won't hurt her. She's just silly.' "

George's father was only slightly amused. He did not approve of practical jokes.

Margaret Dawson was both high-spirited and beautiful— so beautiful that, as a young girl in Scotland, she had once posed as an artist's model, and so high-spirited that she'd married Willian against the wishes of her parents.

She had met William when he'd been a student in Edinburgh. They'd fallen in love but William had had to leave Edinburgh after only one year. It was at this time that his father had lost his ships and William had felt duty-bound to return to Pictou and help pay back the debts. After

1 George's father, William Dawson
2 George's mother, Margaret Mercer Dawson
3 McGill College in 1861

4 The Dawson family at McGill: George, Father, Mother, William, Anna
5 George's sister, Anna
6 The Dawson family and friends at their summer home on the
   St. Lawrence, shortly after George's return from London.

seven years during which they'd written regularly he'd returned to Edinburgh for another year of study, and to claim Margaret as his bride. Her mother had been outraged. She would never consent to have her beautiful daughter carried off by a penniless colonial to live among illiterate pioneers and wild Indians. So Margaret had eloped. Her mother never forgave her.

From his father and grandfather George certainly inherited his determination and zest for work, and from them he learned his love of geology, but from his mother he inherited his high spirits and the blessing of a sense of humor.

In 1855 William Dawson was asked to become Principal of McGill College in Montreal. McGill was in financial trouble and had so few students that it was in danger of having to close. The board of governors asked Sir Edmund Head—then Governor-in-Chief of Canada—to find them a "man of distinction." They thought he would choose someone from Oxford or Cambridge Universities in England, and were dismayed when he selected a colonial from Nova Scotia. But Sir Edmund knew his man. Already George's father had explored and mapped in detail the whole peninsula of Nova Scotia, had won acclaim for his book *Acadian Geology*, and had established a Teacher's College at Truro. Now he was ready to accept the challenge of a new, and more demanding task. Pictou days were over. Sadly the family said good-bye to Grandpa, and left for Montreal.

At first, George and Anna had been homesick in the strange city with its glittering tin roofs, great churches and tall narrow houses with their long staircases reaching from

20

the second story down to the wooden sidewalks. Nearly everybody spoke French, which the children didn't understand. They were lonely for their grandfather, and George was disappointed that he had to study at home. He was glad when William was big enough to join in games; and later he made a friend of Dan O'Hara, the son of a professor who also lived in rooms at the college.

What a great day it had been when he set out for Montreal High School! At last he was going to be like other boys.

Now, after only seven months at school it was all over. At the age of eleven he was ill and crippled.

3
Determination

For three weeks after the onslaught of his disease, George moaned in agony on his bed, his rigid body burning with fever, his unseeing eyes flinching even from the light of a candle. Grandpa Dawson arrived from Pictou and led the family in long and fervent prayers asking Almighty God to forgive them their sins and to spare the beloved child.

At the end of three weeks George's fever began to subside. One morning when Anna tiptoed into the darkened room he opened his eyes and smiled at her.

"What time is it?"

Anna burst into tears.

George tried to turn his head on the pillow.

"What's wrong?" he asked anxiously.

"Shh! nothing now. It's just that you've been so sick. You musn't talk and tire yourself."

"I'm not tired. I want to get out of here," said George.

But he was, in fact, still partly paralyzed and very weak. For the rest of that summer and all the following winter he was confined, first to his bed, then to an invalid's chair. His sickroom was like a prison to him.

"As soon as I get better I'm going to run away and live outdoors in the wilderness forever," he told Anna one day. "I'm going to explore the wilderness. I'm going to collect it and I'm going to bring it home."

"I'll miss you," said Anna, smiling, as she tidied the table by his bedside which was cluttered with shells and fossils and rocks and books and pencils. Usually she had a way of soothing his emotions, but today angry tears stung George's eyes.

"You don't understand. Nobody understands! I feel like a galley slave chained to a deck. I can't move. I can't get the things I need!"

"I'll get you things, George. I'll get you anything," Anna offered.

George heaved a sigh and gave her a twisted grin.

"I know," he said. "You're the best friend in the world. Everybody's good to me. But I want to go fossiling myself. I want to be a geologist. I need to discover and poke about and find things. Papa is kind. He comes in every day and brings me all kinds of specimens and almost anything I want. But . . . ."

He choked and turned his face away, ashamed of his tears. It wasn't often he gave way to despair. He wanted to tell Anna that only the evening before he had overheard a conversation between his mother and father, but he couldn't. The hurt was too deep.

They had come into his room to see him. He hadn't answered when they'd spoken to him and they'd thought he was asleep. Suddenly he'd known that his mother was crying, and his father trying to comfort her. His mother's voice had been a low, sobbing whisper, but the sick boy had heard every word.

"It might have been better if he had died! How can he ever find happiness now? He was always so full of energy—so full of life. Oh, my poor son! My poor son!"

"You musn't rebel against God's will, Margaret. Be glad that George's brain isn't injured. We must be humble and accept this cross."

"But the doctor says his spine is permanently injured. He'll be deformed . . . he . . . . Oh, William! A hunchback!"

"Shh!"

The voices had faded as William Dawson had led his wife out into the hall.

George had stared wide-eyed into the darkness, stunned with shock.

It couldn't be true! God wouldn't let it be true. Grandpa said all sickness and suffering was a form of divine punishment but George knew he had never been so wicked that he deserved to have his whole body twisted out of shape—forever.

That night he lay awake again and the agony of his spirit was far worse than the torture of the physical pain. But he had to suffer alone; he felt it was too terrible to share.

For the rest of his life George could not talk about his deformity—not even to Anna. Later on he knew what his father was trying to tell him when he hired a tutor (a stupid clod of a fellow, in George's opinion) and urged George to study hard and learn all he could "because you'll have to earn your living with your brains. Probably you'll be a professor."

George listened respectfully, but made no comment.

24

In his heart he rebelled. He rejected the God of his father and grandfather—a God who punished small boys with crippling illnesses. He made his own prayers to his own God— One who gave strength to people to overcome their handicaps, if only they had faith and tried hard enough.

From then on he wasted little time in self-pity. He found many interesting things to do even while he remained in bed. It was true that, although his body was crippled, his brain was not.

His father gave him a little printing press so he could print the stories and poems he liked to write. An ingenious boy, he put it to almost immediate use.

His greatest need was for someone to run errands for him. Anna and his mother were the most willing, but a baby brother, Rankine, had been born the year before George started high school, and the toddler required much attention. It was a busy household, with important guests going and coming. Often seven-year-old William and his friends came popping in and out of George's bedroom to see what he was doing. He would ask them to fetch him something—a book from the library, a box of specimens from his father's office, a penny's worth of charcoal—and the boys would promise. But though William was a solemn, conscientious, clever, little boy, and meant well, he often forgot.

More than once George started to lose his temper.

"If I was rich and could pay those boys, they'd remember," he thought one afternoon, and that gave him an idea. For the next few days he was busy with his printing press, turning out play money. William and his friends were delighted.

"See who can earn the most," George suggested craftily; and soon there was keen competition. For a while, at any rate, that problem was solved.

Most of the boys at school soon forgot their sick friend. Dan O'Hara never did, and often he dropped in for a game of checkers or chess. But mostly it was Anna who kept George company. She came to spend many quiet hours during which they sketched and painted with water colours, critized each other's efforts, and held long, intimate conversations. His father came whenever he could, to talk geology and bring interesting visitors; and Grandpa came with his Bible, to give him religious instruction.

The days passed quickly enough but sometimes he couldn't sleep because of pain, and the misery and fear of what the future would bring, and then the nights were long and bitter and lonely.

His family tried to compensate for his affliction by giving him everything possible to keep him occupied. He could easily have developed into a pampered, spoiled, selfish invalid; but somehow he didn't. He was one of those rare unspoilable people with a naturally cheerful disposition and with a keen interest in a multitude of things. And deep within him burned a small, steady light of determination. *Somehow* he was still going to be a geologist.

For seven years George remained a semi-invalid, sometimes able to live an almost normal life, but often afflicted with terrible headaches that kept him in bed for days at a time. The headaches were part of the cruel dwarfing process which gradually crumpled and deformed his spine and prevented him from growing any taller. Although at first

26

he didn't know it, he could never live the life of a normal boy again.

If he had been an ordinary human being he might never have left his wheelchair. But George was not ordinary. For one thing, he could not bear to be idle. Always there were lessons to prepare, books to read, and boxes of specimens from his father's office to be cleaned and sorted and labelled. He was an eager listener to the conversations of the scientists who came to the college to see his father, and he soon found himself joining in their talk. George liked nothing better than a good argument. He had his own ideas on almost every subject. There were times when the men, some of whom took their positions in the world very seriously, thought of George as a cheeky boy, but mostly they liked him. Certainly they all admired his courage and found, often to their surprise, that his ideas were not only fresh but very intelligent. And his unexpected quirks of humour could turn annoyance to sudden laughter.

He was also interested in world affairs and local politics. In 1866 a controversy simmered in Montreal over whether a public park should be made on Mount Royal. George wanted the steep wooded mountain in the heart of the city to remain in its natural state, but when at last the matter was referred to a committee, he decided he would stop worrying. Instead, he wrote a poem on the subject, which was printed in a weekly paper called *Grip*.

27

SENSE FROM A MUDDY SOURCE

Upon Mt. Royal's wooded height
    a slimy pool there lies;
And on its brink the other night
    two frogs conversed this wise—

Oldest inhabitant, was one
    of all the croaking throng;
And troubled sore with rheumatiz
    when he did swim along.

The other had but little sense
    as you right soon will hear,
For when his old companion said,
    (saluting him) "What cheer?"

All trembling in a dreadful fright,
    he thus did make reply,
"They're going to make a park up here,
    Alas for you and I!"

"Tut," said the other, "Do not shake,
    you need not be afraid.
'Twill yet be many years
    ere here a park is made—

"The tadpole's egg is yet unlaid
    that this great park will see,
Oh no, you need not be afraid
    thanks to the Committee."

Then froggie of the little wit
    said, "What's a Committee?"
When quoth the other, "I don't know
    exactly what it be

28

"But if unto a committee
　　the world itself we trust,
'Twould take ten years instead of one,
　　the very poles would rust—

"Now spring again into the pond
　　and croak away with joy,
For we will all be turned to shine
　　ere this park's made, my boy."

G.M.D.

George spent the summers of his teenage years at the sea-shore, sometimes at Tadoussac and sometimes at Cacouna on the Gulf of St. Lawrence about 400 miles northeast of Montreal. It was here that he gained strength to engage a-gain in all the active things he loved. Usually his mother and his two younger brothers went with him. Anna often had to stay at home to help her father and manage the household.

The cool, invigorating climate of the St. Lawrence gulf was better for George's health than the heat and humidity of the city. Life was simple and quiet there. In the French villages, the brightly painted houses, with their wide, over-hanging eaves, stood close together along friendly streets. And, in the countryside, the long narrow farms stretched back from the river like vari-coloured green ribbons, marked off by grey weather-beaten wooden fences. Each house had its own stone-walled well for water, with bal-ance pole and bucket, and also a brick or clay outdoor oven for baking the fine white bread for which French Canadians are still famous. Pedlars came often to cottage doors, bringing fresh fish or farm produce; and occasionally, much to George's amusement, an organ-grinder came with his trained monkey on a string, running around with a red cap to collect pennies.

Although plagued by frequent headaches and easily over-tired, George spent every possible moment outdoors. He collected insects, identified and sketched wildflowers, went fishing, and at low tide, hunted for shells and all sorts of in-tertidal creatures along the shore. The city maid who came to help, lived in constant dread of what he was going to bring home. A shriek from the kitchen would bring Mrs. Dawson on the run, her long skirts caught up in one hand, her pretty mouth twisted with the effort to hide her amusement.

"Oh, George, *must* you?" she would exclaim, peering at a squirming conger eel or a repulsive bladder fish. "Take that outside. Do you really need it for studying—or did you bring it home just to scare Alice?"

And George would go off with his horrible trophies, grin-ning impishly to himself.

He missed Anna, and looked forward to visits from her or his father, or his friend, Dan O'Hara. They seemed to spur him on when he grew tired or discouraged and they brought him things he needed. He wrote Anna frequently, and there was always an order: "I hope you remembered to tell Papa about me wanting the *American Naturalist*, so as to know what to do with my moth eggs, which I mentioned in my last letter. Please ask him to bring all information re-lating to silkworms."

Or: "Bring down the cod liver oil and ask William to get me 2 d's worth of pulverized charcoal."

And again: "Tell Papa, with regard to hand-carriages,

30

that if he can get one suitable for running up and down precipices and through tall woods full of spruce and scrub, it might do very well to carry water for my aquaria!"

Besides all his scientific projects, George worked constantly to improve his skills. When he was seventeen he wrote to tell Anna of his pleasure when his father bought "a very nice gun to amuse myself with at Tadoussac. We had a preliminary trial of it the other evening, and of course everybody must have a shot, so we riddled an unfortunate little box, and cut a row of peas into salad!"

He learned to ride horseback quite by accident one summer when Dan O'Hara was visiting him. The boys were given permission to hire an old nag named Molly and a buckboard, and go off on an all-day picnic. It was the first time George had ever taken a horse by himself, and he was as proud of handling the reins as if he had been a young sport showing off with a thoroughbred stallion. Five miles from home the boys found a shady spot by a little stream. They tied the mare to a tree, ate their sandwiches, and then, of course, George said, "Come on, let's go down to the beach and explore. We'll have to get some good strong sticks for prying up rocks."

"I'll get the wire net and the sack," O'Hara offered.

The tide was low and the wide waters of the Gulf lay before them, blue and sparkling in the summer sunshine. The boys stripped off shoes and stockings, and went barefoot over the rough barnacled rocks. Time passed unnoticed as they filled their sack with everything they could find, including two black lobsters, a dozen crabs and a quart of periwinkles, for O'Hara was more interested in good things to eat than he was in scientific specimens.

31

Suddenly Dan exclaimed, "The tide's coming in! It's getting late!"

George looked up at the western sky.

"Yes, let's go!"

They hurried back to the picnic spot, and stopped short in dismay. Driven desperate by swarming black flies, old Molly had kicked out at the buckboard and broken one of the shafts.

"We should have unharnessed her! How stupid!" cried George.

O'Hara was almost ready to cry.

"What'll we do? It must be a mile to the nearest farm!"

Always practical, George examined the buckboard.

"There's no way we can fix it," he said.

"We'll have to walk," said O'Hara, in despair.

"No, we won't. Didn't you ever ride horseback?"

"A couple of times . . . but . . . ."

"But nothing! Come on, we have to find a way to take this sack. You can sit up front, and I'll cling on behind like a lady."

O'Hara looked at his friend reproachfully.

"Dawson, how can you joke at a time like this?"

"Well, it's funny! Just think, the whole village will come and stare as we ride back in triumph," said George, already scrambling up on Molly's back with great difficulty. Reluctantly O'Hara climbed on in front.

They started off.

"This is great!" exclaimed George, quite delighted with the turn of events. "I'm going to ask my parents if I can have riding lessons."

"Your parents will give you a lesson when they hear about this," O'Hara warned ominously.

Actually, George's mother was more disturbed by her son's temerity in riding the horse than she was about the damage to the abandoned buckboard. When his father heard the story, he said simply that it would be a good thing for George to learn more about horses. Within a few days O'Hara had to return to Montreal, but that summer became George's riding summer. He had the same rapport with animals he had with people, and eventually he became a superb horseman.

At the end of each summer George returned to Montreal. Great changes were taking place at McGill during his teenage years. When the Dawsons had arrived in Montreal in 1855, the college had consisted of one unfinished building, already in a state of disrepair, standing in the middle of a cow-pasture. The staff totalled eight members, who subsisted miserably on starvation wages. No science courses were offered on the curriculum and the only useful thing relating to these subjects was a single piece of coral, which the children had found in the pigeon-hole of a desk.

William Dawson began his work at McGill by bringing with him all the specimens he had collected from his own museum at Pictou and all his own scientific equipment. (He was one of the first to use the microscope as an aid to science.) He was an excellent and patient teacher, and conducted many courses himself, not only in geology, but in paleontology, mineralogy, botany and zoology. He was also a well-known ethnologist, archeologist, agronomist, linguist and theologian.

A man who exhibited great self-confidence, he taught that all things came from God, the Creator, and that a scientist should approach his work humbly and reverently. He believed that self-reliance, application, observation and determination were the qualities of an educated man, and not outword forms and shows. A holiday for him was a chance to plant a garden, climb a mountain, dredge knowledge from the bottom of an ocean, or go on any kind of exploratory trip.

In all these things George wanted desperately to participate, and whenever it was physically possible, his father welcomed him at his side. Yet, for George, this was not enough. He, too, was a born leader. He would never have been content to remain forever a helper or assistant, but as assistant to his father's colleagues he learned a great deal.

George never forgot the spring of 1865 when Dr. Phillip Carpenter came to McGill. He and Anna always called it, "the year of the bad smell." Dr. Carpenter brought with him several tons of shells. They had been collected by a Belgian naturalist in California who had died before he had been able to do anything with them. Dr. Carpenter spent much of the rest of his life with these shells, cleaning, sorting, studying and labelling them (the collection is still in the Redpath Museum in Montreal) but when he first arrived and opened the boxes, the decaying matter inside the shells gave off a dreadful odour—so nauseating, in fact, that new ventilation and a drainage system had to be installed inside the building where the doctor worked. As soon as he could stand the stench, George sometimes worked with him.

In these years, even though he was still at school, George

was sometimes hired to assist the professors. He also developed several hobbies of his own.

One of his hobbies was photography. He had a dark room and a camera, and his father kept him supplied with the glass plates and chemicals for developing negatives by the wet-collodion process used in those days.

On his summer collecting expeditions, George found himself wishing that geologists could use photography on field trips. How much more satisfactory such pictures would be than time-consuming, on-the-spot, sketches! But the equipment necessary was much too heavy or fragile to be practical. It would be very useful, he thought, if a lightweight camera could be invented—one that could take pictures of moving things, like a herd of migrating buffalo.

George was fifteen when Eva, the youngest of the five Dawson children, was born. Anna, with her strong maternal instinct, was delighted with the new arrival, but, to his dismay, George found himself jealous of the time Anna spent with the baby. Without realizing it, he had come to think of his older sister as his own special friend, someone whose affection, support, advice and time belonged to him. It came over him, watching her with Eva, that one day she would marry and have children of her own, and he felt a great sense of desolation. Home without Anna, could never be home. He was very fond of William and Rankine. But Rankine was much too young, and William was so serious. Anna always knew what George was laughing at, but he had to explain to William. Now he began to think more and more about his father's lessons in self-reliance. He threw himself more ardently than ever into his studies and spent more time in the society of his father and his father's scientific colleagues. During the winters he often watched the McGill students having snowfights and snowshoe races, talking of plans that included mountain climbing, parties, and gay evenings with dancing. Sometimes he would look bitterly at his own dwarfed, misshapen body. And sometimes the headaches would overtake him for days and he would lie in bed in his dark room unable to sleep, unable to do anything. There was no medicine to help. All he could do was lie there in pain until the bout was over.

Then he was up, busy and cheerful again. Gradually he began to assert his independence. He insisted on going about by himself and finding his own friends. There was something so compelling about his sparkling blue eyes, so engaging about his ever-ready wit, so dynamic about his personality, that he attracted friends like a magnet. He learned that if he was not self-conscious and simply forgot about any sense of differentness, he could put people at their ease.

In 1868, when he was eighteen, George registered as a part-time student at McGill. He studied English and chemistry and, of course, geology. The following summer he spent at Tadoussac, part of the time at a hotel by himself, where he soon acquired a group of congenial friends. At the end of that summer he wrote to his sister:

My Dear Anna,

I was up till twelve last night looking at the stars, and got up this morning at half-past three, to see a lot of people off from the hotel .... We had a beautiful walk over to the wharf just as the day was breaking, and on the way home, I went up one of the hills and sat down there and waited for the sunrise which was beautiful . . . .

I have become quite troubled by Papa's and Mamma's great anxiety about my coming home alone. Please try and persuade them that their anxiety is quite unnecessary.

The taste of independence was exhilarating.

Somehow he had to convince his parents that he was going to lead a life of his own.

4
Atlantic
Voyage

The year of formal study at McGill and the pleasure of the freedom he had enjoyed during the previous summer at Tadoussac tightened the knot of George's determination to get out of his comfortable home and try his own wings.

That fall, when he was nineteen, he went with his father one afternoon to visit Sir William Logan, who was then head of the Geological Survey of Canada. Sir William was a bachelor with one love—geology. He was seventy years old and no longer able to go on long, arduous expeditions. He lived in a room over the geological museum on the Champs de Mars in downtown Montreal.

The son of a Montreal baker, Sir William had become known as the father of Precambrian geology. His studies of clays and coal seams in Wales and England had resulted in the first geological map of Great Britain, and his pioneer work in Canada included the mapping of areas in Ontario, Quebec and the Gaspé for which no topographical maps had existed. The Geological Survey of Canada had begun under his direction in 1842 and after Confederation in 1867 it had become one of the most important undertakings of the new nation.

George admired Sir William tremendously and he and his father had often visited the distinguished scientist in the museum, but on this day a noisy group of students made conversation difficult.

"Come upstairs to my apartment," invited Sir William. They followed him up a narrow, dark flight of stairs and entered a single small room. There was no carpet on the floor. There were no curtains at the windows. In the centre of the room a kitchen table was cluttered with papers and maps, and rough wooden boxes stood about filled with geological specimens. A washstand occupied one corner. And along one wall there was a narrow cot. From the walls dangled the garments Sir William wore on his expeditions, and lined up on the floor was a parade of well-worn boots. There were no other furnishings.

Sir William smiled at his young visitor's look of surprise.

"These things are all I need, George. Extra gear means extra housework. Life's too short. I'm an old man. There's still so much geology I want to do but I must soon resign my post as head of the Survey. A younger man is needed."

George watched as the two scientists bent their heads together over the table to examine some new specimens of rock. His father's hair was grey, but Sir William's was as white as his long, luxuriant beard. His dress could only be described as careless; George had once overheard someone remark that Sir William always looked as bedraggled as a shipwrecked sailor. But when a man had achieved such re- markable things, outward appearances seemed unimportant.

The two men were totally absorbed in study, and for once George did not join them. As he quietly paced the floor of the small dark room he knew he could not continue to work as an assistant in his father's office. With all its improvements, McGill University could not offer him all that he needed in his field of study. These men had boldly chosen what they wanted from life, and had contributed great things to their country and to the world. They were both largely self-educated, but because of recent advances in science, this kind of training was no longer good enough.

There was a special university in London—the Royal School of Mines—which offered the best course of study in the world for geologists. On its staff were famous men of science, and George longed to learn from them. He thought of how his father had become a geologist and an educator in spite of Grandpa Dawson's efforts to make him into a preacher of the Gospel. He, too, would have to take a stand.

To continue the work of Sir William Logan, to mark new places on the map of Canada, to be a leader of expeditions—that was his dream. It had always been his dream—and he was going to make it come true.

That night he made a startling announcement to his family. He wanted to leave Montreal and McGill and go to England to study geology at the Royal School of Mines.

His mother was as shocked as George had expected, but his father saw at once that his son had made up his mind, and voiced no objection. Instead he did everything he could to help him. He ordered the manufacture of a special collapsible invalid's chair so that George could sit comfortably at an ordinary desk. He wrote to his friend, Sir Charles Lyell, in London, and to other prominent scientific men of his acquaintance who lived there, to tell them of his son's courageous decision. He hoped they would stand by in case of trouble.

And so it came about that George Dawson was accepted and enrolled as a student at the Royal School of Mines. He could hardly believe it when he found himself standing on the deck of the sailing packet *Lake Erie* on a bright September morning, waving good-bye to his family. They looked unreal, like miniature china figurines grouped together on the dock. There was Papa, tall and stately in his black frock coat and stovepipe hat and, anchored to his arm, Mamma floating in her billowy hoop skirt like a lavender balloon about to take off. William was all arms and legs and as gawky and ill at ease as any teenager, while Rankine was darting in and out among the crowd like a squirrel, no doubt getting in everyone's way. It was a good thing little Eva had been left at home with the servants. And Grandpa was missing. Though he had come to spend his last years in Montreal he had not felt well enough to take the long horse-cab drive to the dock.

George's gaze rested longest on the graceful figure of Anna, grown up now at seventeen, in a tiny flowered bonnet, carrying a frilled white parasol and wearing a pastel-embroidered hoop skirt almost as big as Mamma's. She stood quietly by herself, sometimes waving the white handkerchief which George knew was wet with tears. He was glad that Bernard Harrington, professor of chemistry at McGill, had not joined the family for this special occasion. He felt a familiar pang of jealousy, which he had told himself over and over was ridiculous. It would be dreadful —unthinkable—if his lovely sister never had any suitors—for

41

what career was there for a girl but marriage and mother-hood? Did he want Anna doomed to a life of despised spinsterhood? George liked Harrington, he liked him very much. Still, he was glad the professor was not there today to comfort his weeping sister. He dashed a hand across his own eyes and tried to call her above the clamour of departure.

"Anna!"

But of course she couldn't hear him.

At last the boat pulled away from the dock, Anna's waving handkerchief could be seen no more, and George, fascinated, watched the manoeuvres of the two tugs which were towing the *Lake Erie* out into the channel of the St. Lawrence River. Suddenly he realized something had gone wrong. Caught in the swift current at an awkward angle, the vessel drifted sideways, and despite the frantic efforts of the tugboatmen, a quarter of an hour later she ran aground just opposite Richelieu wharf.

George burst out laughing.

"What's so funny?"

The red-headed young man leaning on the rail looked down at him.

"My father was so careful about the ship I was to sail on. He made enquiries for weeks! The *Lake Erie* had the best record—and now she runs aground even before she leaves harbour!"

The red-head grinned, then he frowned.

"Do you think it's a bad omen?"

He knocked superstitiously on the wooden rail with his freckled knuckles.

George said he doubted it and introduced himself. It

turned out that Karl Rimmer was booked to share a cabin with him.

George took it for granted that his companion was just as excited about the voyage as he was. He kept up a running comment about what was happening to the vessel as the sailors tried to get her afloat and under way again. Rimmer was astonished by George's knowledge of nautical proceedings.

"How do you know so much about ships, Dawson?" he asked.

"Oh, it's mostly book-learning—but I'm taking lessons in navigation on this trip."

Rimmer's eyebrows lifted in surprise.

"Navigation? Do you plan to be a ship's officer?"

It was a thoughtless question. How could a little hunchback become a ship's officer? *Poor fellow*, thought Rimmer. But George looked up at him with untroubled eyes, and told him about his plans.

"Navigation can be useful on land as well as on sea. Anyway, I'm curious about things," he concluded.

"I believe it! What a load of books you've got! And what about that other stuff? Why all the rope? And the nets?"

George laughed.

"Who knows? If we spot a mermaid, we'll have a go at catching her!"

Rimmer did not understand. He didn't make jokes like that himself, he read few books and had no interest in studying. He was an English boy returning home from a visit to Canada. He said he was going to learn a trade, and would probably become a mechanic. His equipment for whiling away the tedious weeks ahead was a pack of playing cards. He had watched and listened to the Dawson family saying good-bye to his cabin mate.

"Don't forget your pills. . . . Be careful not to get wet. . . . Get plenty of rest. . . . Oh, George, be careful in those dreadful London fogs!"

George had noticed Rimmer's look of disgust at all this pampering and he saw the puzzled look that was there now. He said nothing.

The first part of the journey down the St. Lawrence was pleasant, with warm, sunny days. George spent every possible moment on deck, taking lessons with the quadrant, and talking to the pilot who had to guide the ship to the open waters of the Gulf. Each night the ship had to cast anchor, and set sail again in the early dawn.

Rimmer seemed bored and uninterested. He found others who liked to play cards. George thought this a waste of time. His father never indulged in games, and had taught his children that idleness in any form was wicked. William Dawson always kept a tray of unclassified geological specimens on the window-sill of his office so that any moments that had to be spent in waiting could be usefully employed. Whenever he called a cab, for instance, he worked at sorting and studying these specimens until the very moment the horses drew up at the door. George felt the same way. When he was doing nothing else he wrote poems and letters. Throughout his voyage he kept a log and jotted down everything that interested him.

On 13 September he recorded:
Got anchor up and under way at 6 a.m. . . . It has been a fine warm day with a beautiful sunset over the north

shore mountains . . . made two sketches . . . a great many white porpoises round ship all afternoon and evening, about 8 o'clock counted 32 blowing in thirty seconds. The pilot said that formerly there was a regular cod and halibut fishery off Green Island, though now they are not caught in profitable quantities higher than Father Point . . . . He said sea cows [walruses] were once caught all up the river, the farmers using strips of their thick skins for *calèche* straps . . . Mille Vache Shoal was called after these animals. . . . Pilot left us at Bic at 5 a.m. . . . Fresh breezes, braced up and trimmed the sails. I find time passes very lazily, especially with regard to reading, the soft splashing of the water and the noise of the sails seem to exercise a mesmeric effect and keeps one from understanding anything but the most simple books . . . going 6 1/2 knots. . . .

Four days later the *Lake Erie* sighted the most south-westerly point of Newfoundland. George made a note of it. Friday, 17 September: 6 a.m. Hauled up for Cape Ray all stem sails braced up . . . set fore and afters . . . saw several ships. Noon, fresh breezes from east. . . . 8 p.m. water very phosphorescent. . . . Had over the towing net and got several rich hauls—jellyfish, etc.

On Saturday, 18 September, he wrote:
Light winds and clear weather. Saw a number of small birds, some sparrows, but mostly a small olive and grey fly-catcher, they were about the ship all day; also a hawk which caught and ate one of them. I caught several of the fly-catchers and put them in the cabin, where they

flew about and caught flies for some time. . . . Saw several whales blowing.

By 21 September the *Lake Erie* was in the open Atlantic and fighting bad weather. George kept his log faithfully: 11 a.m. threatening to blow by sudden puffs . . . later blowing hard. Close reefed the three topsails. Noon, strong gale with a very heavy topping sea, ship making very bad weather of it . . . cabin filled with water, first from soil lockers, afterwards on the port side. Large quantities of water continually on deck, rushing from side to side as the ship rolls. Sometimes shipped heavy seas in succession and righted with difficulty . . . cargo shifting. . . . Cabin stove broke adrift. . . . Mate nearly washed overboard.

The weather got worse. It seemed as if Rimmer's superstitious worry had come true, and the *Lake Erie* was doomed to go down in mid-Atlantic, but George wasn't at all upset. He thrilled to the drama and excitement of a great storm at sea. Rimmer was frightened and seasick, and couldn't understand how George still found his way about the ship, carrying out his various projects.

One wild night, when the wind shrieked through the rigging, George struggled across the rolling deck. Cold salt spray slashed across his face, half blinding him, and he had to cling to the railings to keep from being washed overboard. He wrenched open his cabin door just in time to see Rimmer clamber over the side of the bunk, lose his balance, and roll helplessly over and over across the flooded floor.

"Help! Help!" he spluttered.

George burst out laughing.

"Swim, boy, swim!" he shouted.

On the next roll of the ship Rimmer managed to grasp the rail of the bunk, and pull himself up. He looked around and glared furiously at George.

"You wretch! If the ship was foundering you'd find something funny about it."

George bit his lip.

"Sorry, Rimmer. Hang on. I'll get the steward."

But he wasn't very sorry. He couldn't help feeling a sense of inner satisfaction that the big, healthy red-head had proved a weakling, while he had been able to carry on.

When the violence of that particular storm had lessened, and the steward had mopped up the floor and had a fire going again in the little iron stove, Rimmer sat in a chair sipping hot broth.

"How is it you never get seasick, Dawson?" he asked, enviously.

George grinned.

"Oh, I get seasick, but I don't give in. You shouldn't lie about in your bunk so much. Get up and do things."

Rimmer groaned.

"Do things! How can you do things when you're sick?"

For a moment George didn't answer. He stared bitterly at his special invalid's chair. Then he said quietly, "I'm going out on deck to see what it's like, now that the storm is abating. Want to come?"

Rimmer shook his head.

"I couldn't make it. I'm too weak."

George stepped out onto the slippery deck. He looked down. The deck was awash with hundreds of little luminescent sea-creatures. How curious! Ah, this was the sort of thing a fellow missed if he sat and brooded in a corner. He caught several and put them in a bucket to take inside to show to Rimmer. *Poor fellow*, he thought.

Rimmer was feeling better. He was surprised to see this strange collection of small creatures from the depths of the ocean tossed up by the storm. They glowed and flickered like many-coloured fireflies in the dimly lit cabin. He shared George's sense of dismay when the brilliant lights suddenly faded and went out, and there was nothing in the bucket but a limp grey mass.

"They're dead! But they had enough water to keep them alive!"

"I believe they died of fright," said George, solemnly.

The incidents of that evening marked the beginning of a new relationship between the two young men. From then on Rimmer took more and more interest in George's projects, and the cardplayers often had to find someone else for the table. He even began teasing, and he called George's specimens the Endesmodes, a word he made up late one night and which they both enjoyed.

Days passed, and weeks. One gale followed another. The ship was driven far off course, and the cargo of grain in her hold shifted so that when the *Lake Erie* wallowed in the trough of a mountainous sea, she righted herself more and more sluggishly. Often it was too rough for reading or studying, and George's lessons in navigation came to an end, but whenever the seas subsided enough to make it practical he rigged up his towing net and put it over the side. Now Rimmer was there to help him.

It took twenty-six days for the *Lake Erie* to cross the Atlantic. The two boys were as glad as anyone aboard when when, on 5 October, a sailor went up the rigging and cried out that he could see the Irish coast about seventeen miles away. The long stormy voyage was nearly over, and three days later Rimmer and Dawson said good-bye.

They felt sad. They had grown to like one another in spite of their differences. It was a triumph for George, making a friend of a boy like Karl Rimmer, someone who would only have pitied him in any other circumstances. It was a new kind of friendship and he felt truly sorry that they would probably never meet again.

Vowing to write—promises they both really knew they weren't like to keep—they said good-bye and went their separate ways.

By stagecoach and train, surrounded by people with strange accents and ways, George was bound for London to begin a new adventure.

5
London

George sat, pen poised over his ink-pot, waiting for his first class in paleontology to begin at the School of Mines. A hush fell over the room as the famous Professor Sir Edward Frankland entered, carrying with him a glass box. Placing the box in full view of the class he began.

"Three years ago I put a dead cat in this container. It is carefully and completely surrounded by layers of fine charcoal. Normally when animals die, decomposition takes place, and in a very short time nothing is left. Therefore it was very puzzling to early scientists to discover fossilized forms of complete animals, such as the common trilobite. Why had there been no decay before the great weight of earth accumulated which turned the animal to stone? Then it was discovered that under certain circumstances, natural embalmment takes place. Let me show you . . . after three years no decomposition has taken place in my dead cat."

To prove his point, Professor Frankland lifted the cover of the container, bent over and took several long, loud sniffs. He lifted his head and smiled at the class.

"As sweet as a rose," he announced.

This struck George funny, and he laughed.

Professor Frankland was angry.

"This was not intended as a circus trick," he said coldly.

"I beg your pardon, sir."

Sir Edward finished his lecture in a few angry words and left the room. The entombed cat remained on his desk. There was an embarrassed silence, for in those days a professor was treated with great respect. George turned to the black-bearded student next to him.

"Let's go and take a sniff for ourselves," he suggested.

Several of the others grinned and followed him to the front of the room. George leaned over the box and took a deep breath.

"Sweet as a rose!" he mimicked.

Everybody laughed.

George's action was a cover-up for his feelings. Inside he was upset by what had happened. Never before had he made such a bad impression on a teacher. Maybe it was because he had been self-conscious and over-anxious in his strange surroundings. All the excitement which had buoyed his spirits from the day he had made the decision to start out on a career of his own seemed to collapse like a pricked balloon. He needed someone to talk to and he turned to the boy who had sat in the next seat. He introduced himself.

"Dawson—George Dawson—from Canada."

"I'm Pinchey—Archie Pinchey."

They shook hands.

"Come on over to my digs," Pinchey invited, and George accepted gratefully.

They went out into the noisy streets where horsedrawn omnibuses rattled over the cobbles, hawkers cried their wares, and top-hatted, gloved gentlemen and bonneted ladies with great full skirts took up more than their share of space on the crowded sidewalks.

Pinchey's lodgings were not far from Jermyn Street and the School of Mines. They climbed three flights of stairs to a dark attic. Archie, who was almost as tall as a lamp post, couldn't stand upright under the dusty rafters.

"Not much space, but the best I can afford."

He shivered as he touched a sulphur match to the few coals in the grate.

"Sometimes there are advantages to being short," George commented wryly.

He perched on the edge of a rickety chair. He was still worried about getting off to a bad start with Professor Frankland.

"My family says I'm possessed by a wicked sense of humour," he told Pinchey. "My brother William is a serious chap. He never gets into this sort of trouble."

Pinchey was sympathetic.

"Well, maybe the professor won't hold a grudge. He's a very big man, you know."

George was silent as his host began to work a pair of wheezy leather bellows to encourage the smouldering coals. Pinchey glanced up over his shoulder.

"Frankland is none other than the man who evolved the theory of valence, and helped to discover helium," he said.

"Yes, I know," said George.

Pinchey gave him a surprised look.

"It seems odd, your knowing . . . coming from Canada, I mean."

"Why?"

"I've always thought of the American colonies as a great wilderness with Indians and bears and a few log cabins scattered about. But you seem so—well, so cultured."

George laughed. For a minute he forgot Professor Frankland and his cat.

"You remind me of a story my father tells of how, when he was here in England a few years ago, someone at a debating club congratulated him on speaking English so well. My father says, 'Probably the man supposed my native tongue to be Chippewa or Micmac.' "

"My dear fellow . . . I'm sorry . . . I didn't mean. . . ." Pinchey's voice trailed off into an unintelligible mumble as he hastily took down two cracked mugs and placed them on the bare table for the tea which was beginning to steam on the hob.

"My father is Principal of McGill College in Montreal," George explained. "It's a young school and when he took over in 1855 there were no science courses, but now there's a splendid museum, and we have an excellent professor of chemistry—who happens to be in love with my favorite sister."

"How many in your family?" asked Pinchey.

"Five."

George felt a stab of homesickness as he went on to tell about his brothers and sisters. In a few minutes the two young men were exchanging reminiscences over their tea. Pinchey, an only child, had led a secluded early life and told of a pleasant but rather routine career at school. George talked about Nova Scotia and his grandfather, of Anna and his life in Montreal, of his father and his interests and achievements, but the subject of cats was close to the front of his mind, and he recalled a half-forgotten anecdote.

"It was in Montreal, and I was about nine. The McGill governors came to call on my father. I was playing alone in the nursery, cracking walnuts on the floor, when our puss came along and got her paw stuck in one of the shells. It was funny! I got the idea of fitting her out with half a shell on each paw—skates, you know. Poor puss skittered around and got herself tangled up in the string of a toy. It was a tin monkey that beat on a drum when you pulled it along. She nearly went crazy, and before I could stop her she slid into the front parlour where the governors and my father were holding their meeting."

Pinchey laughed.

"I envy you your happy home life."

Pinchey lit up a long white clay pipe, loosened his stiff celluloid collar, and stretched his tightly trousered legs towards the glowing coals in the fireplace. George pulled his own chair closer.

"You haven't told me yet how you happened to come to the School of Mines," said Pinchey.

George held out his hands toward the fire which had done little to take the damp chill out of the room.

"You're right in thinking that much of Canada is still wilderness. Britain has just bought all of Rupert's Land from the Hudson's Bay Company. We call it the Northwest Territories—thousands and thousands of unmapped square miles which should be rich in minerals and other natural resources. I want to be part of that mapping—and the exploring that goes with it. But if I am to get on Canada's Geological Survey I've got to have a good education. So you see why I'm rather worried about Professor Frankland. If he thinks I'm just a clown . . . . I say, Pinchey, you don't suppose he'll refuse me his class?"

Pinchey puffed thoughtfully.

"Of course not. He's too big a man for that. Forget it, old chap."

George stared into the red coals, and then abruptly he pulled out his watch, and got to his feet.

"It's late. We have lessons to do. I'll see you in class," he exclaimed, pulling on his greatcoat. He had made up his mind that Professor Frankland would soon realize that he was not at the School of Mines for fun.

Pinchey lighted his way down the narrow staircase with an end of a candle and George found himself on the street in one of those London fogs his mother had been worried about. He was smothered in an atmosphere so thick that he had to feel his way along the almost deserted sidewalks. Somehow he got to Piccadilly Circus where people were going about with flaming torches, and horses led by their bridles followed men carrying lanterns. Even the gas lights on street posts could not be seen from one dim glowing circle to the next. He was greatly relieved when he found his own door without mishap. His throat felt raw and sore from the smoky vapour.

"Montreal weather is better than this," he muttered to himself.

All the same he was happy to be in London. He had the

natural ability to adjust quickly to any situation and there was something new and stimulating to discover in the great city every day.

He settled down to his work with zest. He was quietly respectful in Professor Frankland's class. No student was more serious than George. The fact that he had had little formal education proved to be only a minor barrier. In this way his illness had served him well. He had read much; he had a vast range of interests, an instant comprehension, and a prodigious memory. He had always associated freely with his father's colleagues, so he was perfectly at ease in any company, and his engaging personality won him friends wherever he went.

As he always had, George worked hard, and was careful not to get too involved socially with groups of students and their parties and outings.

He had many invitations from his father's learned friends, however, and these he usually accepted. Sir Charles Lyell invited him for Christmas.

It was Sir Charles who had "discovered" William Dawson in Pictou. The British scientist had gone to Nova Scotia for a geological tour, and George's father had acted as his guide Amazed by the young man's self-acquired knowledge, Sir Charles had found himself agreeing with William Dawson's ideas on the formation of the coal beds and on other scientific subjects. It was he who had strongly recommended to Sir Edmund Head that William Dawson was the man for McGill.

Lyell had written the most important geological textbooks in use at the School of Mines. He had originated the method of dividing the Tertiary period of geological time into the Eocene, Miocene and Pliocene epochs.

Professor Frankland also was an occasional guest at the Lyell's and got to know George personally. At first their encounters were stiff and formal but before long, when the two met, there were hours spent deep in talk about paleontology. It wasn't just George's charm—which might have failed him this time; it was his insatiable hunger for learning which the older scientist, recognizing a kindred spirit, couldn't resist.

George did not always accept invitations. He enjoyed good company, but he was a doer—he hated watching. He once wrote to Anna:

Last night I was at Sir Charles Lyell's. It turned out to be quite an evening party, dancing, etc. It was Leonard Lyell's 21st birthday. Huxley, Tyndall and Dr. Frankland, etc. were there, so it was quite a distinguished throng . . . but I always feel it a bother that I never learned dancing, it is so uncomfortable to go dodging about on the outskirts and looking at books you don't care to see.

In any case, there was always the excuse that he had to study, or the very real one that he had another of his bad headaches.

Whenever George wanted a break from his studies he went for long walks. He walked because he wanted to sightsee, and at the same time he wanted to save the price of cab-fares. But most of all he walked because he wanted to keep fit. He knew it wouldn't be enough for him to pass his courses at the School of Mines if he wanted to make his dreams come true. He needed to excel, and he needed to have splendid physical stamina. Walking was the best way to develop the strength of his small frame, and, besides, he could always be on some useful errand or enjoy his hobby of people-watching.

His letters to Anna were full of observations:

I saw quite a new trade today, namely a ragged little girl, with a pretty good voice, however, going up the middle of the street singing hymns and eagerly picking up the coppers which some people threw from the windows to her.

There was a soap-box orator at Battersea, who seemed to be preaching "hell-fire and brimstone" every time George passed. "He is missing his front teeth. I think he must have blown them out in a moment of special vehemence."

Outside Kew Gardens in April he saw ". . . hundreds and hundreds of people enjoying themselves in a rougher way than is allowed in the Gardens, waltzing to cracked fiddles and wheezing accordions, playing at Kiss in the Ring, eating periwinkles, shrimps and oranges."

Probably the only time he was late for a class was when he stopped to see Queen Victoria pass in state on her way to the opening of the Holborn Viaduct and Blackfriar's Bridge, ". . . she was not even in her state carriage . . . the whole procession consisted of just a detachment of Horse Guards, then two open carriages with the gentlemen and ladies in waiting . . . then an open carriage with the Queen, Prince Leopold and Princess Beatrice and Louise. The Queen looked quite blooming. Someone near me said, 'How jolly she looks!' . . . "

Archie Pinchey often accompanied George on his walks.

They visited all the great landmarks—St. Paul's Cathredal, Westminster Abbey, the Tower of London, Buckingham Palace and the art galleries, but most often they went to the British Museum. The first time they went, George insisted on seeing the display of stuffed birds and animals from Canada and he was distressed to find there was only a small exhibit.

"It's a disgrace," he told Pinchey. "Some day I'm going to fill in those gaps. We have dozens, maybe hundreds of species of birds and animals that should be on display here."

"But you're a geologist!"

"I can collect more than minerals in my travels. You should see the things Sir William Logan brought back from his expeditions."

They walked on until George stopped to peer into a glass case at a small kangaroo from Australia.

"Now there's a fine bit of work. We have a first-rate taxidermist at our museum. He taught me a good bit about the art."

"You mean you know how to stuff and mount animals—yourself? Is there anything you can't do, Dawson?" exclaimed Pinchey.

The first term passed swiftly—more swiftly than he could have imagined on his first nervous day with Sir Edward Frankland's dead cat. He was planning on working for a summer in Scotland, but before that his mother and father came to London, mainly to see him.

Of course George wanted to hear all the news from home. He learned that Anna and Bernard Harrington were still happiest in each other's company; that William, as quiet and serious as ever, had excelled in his last year at high school and planned to enter the faculty of engineering at McGill in the fall; that Rankine was a bit of a harum-scarum and promised to be much too handsome for his own good; that Anna petted little Eva so much she would probably spoil her; that his friend O'Hara had become a banker.

And there was trouble in Canada—almost a civil war. George had seen a few Canadian newspapers but they were out of date and he wanted to know what was happening in Red River. What did Papa know of Louis Riel? How serious had the rebellion been? What was going on in the West?

His father filled in the details for him as well as he could, and told how troops had been sent by steamer to Port Arthur to enforce law and order.

"It's a terrible journey, I understand, involving half a hundred portages, the cutting of trails and the building of bridges—but of course Canadian soldiers can't enter the United States to follow the usual route. It may be months before the men reach Fort Garry."

The West! George hung on every word. Forgotten were the heavy draped windows, framed portraits of the Royal Family, the ornate candelabras reflected in the mirror over the fireplace of the hotel lounge where they sat. In his imagination he was tramping with the troops in the Northwest, smelling the tangy fresh air, tasting a freshly caught lake trout broiled over the coals of a campfire. He recalled himself with a start when a servant came with tea.

His parents went with him to Scotland for a brief holiday, and together they waited anxiously for the results of George's final exams.

At last the letter came and George tore it open with

trembling fingers, and his eyes raced over the lines.

My dear Dawson,

    I am sorry to have to tell you that you have just missed the scholarship, Milford being before you . . . . I have passed second class in chemistry, thanks to your help and you urging me to work, but not in physics . . . . That beast Prof. Guthrie has only passed about six or seven fellows at most, they were all in a deuce of a wax who did not get through. . . . Excuse this short scribble . . . .

    Believe me, yours sincerely,

    Archie Pinchey

George was elated. Second in the class! After a bad start, second in the class! First would have been better, but second was good. Three years to go and then he would have his doctorate, if he could keep up this high standing. Then back to Canada—and to the Northwest!

George enjoyed his geological field work in the rugged land of his grandfather. (Grandpa was dead now, and it was George who carried the brown cairngorm in his pocket.) He visited the Grampian Hills, the valley of Glenavon and even Kildrummy Castle—romantic places which had figured in his grandfather's story of how he had walked 180 miles, from Keith to Greenock, back in the year 1811 when he had left Scotland with scarcely a penny to his name.

Back in London, George was soon established in his old diggings and deep in his studies again. He followed the same strict routine that had worked for him the first year, and at the end of this term he stayed in the city for four nerve-wracking weeks waiting for marks to be posted. Standings at the end of the second year were very important at the School of Mines. The Director's Medal for coming first in geology, the most coveted of all the awards, was given at that time.

George had made an excellent standing throughout the year and he had great hopes for the medal but he had had keen competition. The suspense was all but unbearable. By the time the day came he was convinced both that he *had* to win and that he couldn't possibly win. He was prepared for anything, he thought; but he wasn't prepared for what happened when he entered the school. He was mobbed by friends.

"Here he is!"

"Dawson! Congratulations!"

"Here! Shake hands, old chap!"

But George couldn't see over the heads of the crowd gathered about the bulletin boards.

"Don't you know? You've won the medal! The Director's Medal! "

They lifted him up on their shoulders then and gave him three cheers. He was a popular winner. All but the sorest losers took pride in his success.

When the excitement had subsided a little, George discovered that not only had he won the Director's Medal, he had won a prize of books for coming first in mineralogy, and a scholarship granted by the Prince of Wales for making the highest standing in his class for the year.

It was a great day. For a little while the taste of success made his head swim, and he seemed to float rather than walk as he made his way home. But he soon came down to earth, and the next night he wrote a modest letter to Anna:

. . . I was very much surprised on going up yester-

day to be received with congratulations on all sides
. . . Prof. Ramesay told me I got 99 out of 100 . . .
the medal is bronze. It has Sir R. Murchison's head
on one side and a trophy of fossils and hammers on
the other, the whole being surrounded by a wreath
of graftolites.

For two more years George worked and studied, summer
and winter, in the British Isles. He was becoming both
learned and practised in his field.

He was also discovering things of deep personal impor-
tance. At this time people all over the world had been
rocked by Charles Darwin's explosive theory of evolution,
and it happened that Thomas Henry Huxley, a noted scientist who had given up a career in biological research in order
to publicize Darwin's theories, was a professor of George's.
Sir Charles Lyell, too, had worked hard to popularize Darwin's proposition but George's own father was deeply
shocked by the idea of evolution, and had written several
theological books to disprove and discredit the theory.

George himself had an open mind. He listened closely to
Huxley's brilliant teaching. He himself had come to question some of the dogmas of the Presbyterian Church, and
for the rest of his life his church attendance was somewhat
irregular. This became a sore point between him and the
rest of his family. In one of his letters to Anna he put the
matter bluntly:

My Dear Anna,
I do not particularly object to your sermons, as
you seem to think I do, except in so far as they oc-
cupy space which might be devoted to other subjects.

Believing as you do, you cannot help feeling as you say, but I am sure you would be the last person in the world to ask anyone to try to make themselves believe in that which does not appear reasonable to them, for this would be mental dishonesty.

Yet his personal religion remained constant, and when he was much older he wrote a poem, about his belief in a life after death.

> . . . But still I cannot think that all must be
> in vain
> Thought is too subtle, too intense
> To die and have no place.
> Love is too deep and hope too high.

George finished in England in the spring of 1873 and on 16 June he sailed from Liverpool for Montreal. With him, he carried his degree of doctor of science and the highest honours awarded by the Royal School of Mines. He also had the affection and admiration of his classmates. Archie Pinchey told him sadly that he'd never have another friend like him.

Sir Edward Frankland had been among those who had made every effort to keep the brilliant young Canadian in England. George had even been offered a professorship at the School of Mines. But he was not tempted by offers of prestige or money. In his pocket he had a letter of acceptance from Canada.

10 February, 1873

Sir:

I have the honour to inform you, that by an Order in Council passed on the 6th instant, you have been appointed to the position of Naturalist and Botanist on the British North American Boundary Commission of which Cameron, R.A., is the Commissioner, at a salary of $2,000.00 per annum, the same to take effect as soon as your services are required.

    I have the honour to be Sir

    Your obedient servant

    J. C. Aikens, Sec'y of State

To George the letter was greater by far than the Director's Medal or the diploma from the School of Mines. To be a member of the British section of the North American Boundary Commission! He had scarcely dared hope, when he made application. that they would consider him for a post. But here it was in writing. He was to have a part in the task of marking the border between Canada and the United States from the Lake of the Woods to the Rocky Mountains. It was the beginning of his dream-come-true.

6
Home

George arrived home from England in early spring of 1873, a momentous year in the history of Canada—the year the Boundary Commission began its work, Prince Edward Island joined Confederation, and the Royal Canadian Northwest Mounted Police was formed.

There was as yet no word from the Commission to tell George exactly when he would be wanted, but meanwhile it was great to be back in Canada. Many changes had taken place in his family and among his friends, too. As he had noted in a letter to Anna from London, "Whenever a fellow leaves home, awful things seem to happen and people die, get born, or married just as if they were afraid to do it while he's there."

George found that Rankine at fourteen had become a tall handsome boy who made good marks at school. With fine features and dark, glowing eyes and a mercurial disposition, he was totally different from quiet William who was now doing post-graduate work at McGill in Applied Science and Engineering. At nine, Eva still played with dolls, but she liked better to dress up and parade around in her big sister's bonnets and parasols.

And Anna? Anna was the same Anna she'd always been, only grown up. She was still his best friend, as she'd been his best friend in Pictou and all through his long illness and in all the letters they'd exchanged during his London days. He couldn't wait to get the chance to talk to her alone. But the household was so busy! Old friends dropping in to welcome him home and to congratulate him on his achievements, new members of the faculty at McGill who wanted to meet him.

He had to get used to being addressed as Dr. Dawson—a queer but exhilarating feeling. It was necessary to distinguish him from his father and he soon gained the title of Dr. George. He liked it.

He wanted to see all the changes and improvements in the buildings and facilities at the university and he wanted to get into the city to see what had happened there. But most of all he wanted to see Anna alone. He found her one hot, sunny afternoon in the sewing room.

"I'm going for a stroll around the campus. Come and join me when you can," he urged. Anna put down her sewing.

"I'll come now," she offered.

Even in the heat and humidity she managed to look cool and sweet under her frilled parasol. Her long white skirts rustled as she moved gracefully over the smooth green campus lawn.

"Remember the first day we came here from Nova Scotia?" she asked, smiling down at her brother.

"Of course I do! Everyone gabbling away in French as we clattered through the streets."

"And there was McGill in a cow pasture."

"With a cross cow in it," added George. "That cow used to chase me every time I went down to the brook to play."

Anna laughed, then sobered.

"How upset Mamma was when she saw what a state the building was in! Remember the way we had to climb over the weeds and rubble to get into the east wing? All those cobwebs swaying like tattered curtains? But it didn't take her long to get everyone busy with buckets and mops."

"It was fun sleeping on the floor the first night—except for the rats," said George.

Anna giggled, and impulsively George caught her hand.

"Everything here has changed—and improved—including you Anna! I think you've grown beautiful. Harrington is the luckiest man in the world."

Anna blushed and twirled her parasol.

"Nothing is finally decided yet, you know. But what about you, George?"

George's sensitive mouth, framed by its neatly-trimmed beard, hardened and he did not answer. They came to a low bench and Anna sank down upon it. Her fashionable tight corset, almost unbearably uncomfortable in the heat, made her short of breath. George sat on the grass at her feet, apparently admiring the bright flower beds and the small ornamental trees. Finally he said, "No woman can follow where I plan to go."

"Don't dismiss my sex so lightly," said Anna, flicking open a carved ivory fan.

"Oh, I'm a Woman's Rights man. Most females are tiresome company because their minds are occupied with such small and stupid things. There should be women geologists—and chemists!"

"Now you're poking fun at me," said Anna.

"No, I'm serious. Papa is right. Women should be allowed to attend universities—if only to make better companions for their husbands. Most of them don't know any more than a cat. I don't mean you, Anna!"

But Anna didn't want to argue. She placed a hand gently on her brother's thick brown hair.

"You haven't changed much, George, except for your beard and your silly English accent. We're all so glad to have you home. Do you *have* to go west with the Boundary Commission? Couldn't you still change your mind and accept a professorship at McGill?"

George turned away from her and carefully pulled a starry white chickweed from the lawn.

"If we're going to have a country that commands some respect in the world, we need more than just a boundary line to mark us off from the United States. We need to settle the Northwest—and before that we need to know what's out there."

Anna fanned her hot face.

"But why do you feel that's your job, George? Papa says you now have more academic training than any geologist in Canada!"

George looked up to see tears sparkling in his sister's eyes.

"Oh, Anna, I *must* go! You know that! How can you urge me to bury myself alive? You, of all people!"

"I know, George. But Mamma worries so about you . . . ."

"I'm quite well and strong! I've tramped for the past three summers over mountainous terrain in Scotland, and I feel better when I'm out-of-doors. All my life I've wanted

69

to explore Canada! I just wish the Boundary Commission would stop squabbling and get on with their business."

"You must live your life the way you want, George—but I miss you so when you're away," said Anna.

George felt a pang of deep sadness. This was his real good-bye to Anna, and to the years they had shared so closely.

"You're the one who gave me courage when I needed it most, Anna. It's because of you I'm able to build a life of my own."

They fell silent.

Eva came bouncing up and broke the solemn moment. "It's time for tea. Everyone is waiting for you," she scolded.

They strolled back across the campus together.

Usually George managed to avoid emotional scenes. He was at loose ends now, waiting for word that his services were needed at the boundary. So when a chance came to go to Cape Breton to make a report on the coal beds in the Port Hood area, he accepted gratefully. Once more he sailed down the St. Lawrence.

For this work he received one hundred dollars. It seems a small sum, but in those days when butter sold for eighteen cents a pound, it was good pay. Within a few weeks the job was finished, he was back in Montreal, and the call came to go west.

The boundary between the United States and Canada from Lake of the Woods to the Rocky Mountains was to go along the 49th Parallel. That had been decided in 1818 but the Commission hadn't been set up until 1872. In September, 1872, the headquarters of the two surveying camps had already been established: the Americans at Fort Pembina, in Minnesota, and the British just north of them in temporary barracks at Dufferin, Manitoba. It had been agreed that the marking of the boundary should begin at the northwest angle of Lake of the Woods, where, in 1824, a reference monument had been placed.

But almost at once there was an argument, because this marker couldn't be located. When at last it was found and measurements taken, it was learned that the marker had been inaccurately placed—and that meant that Canada's custom house at Pembina was not even in Canada, but in the United States! No more work was done that fall, but in the spring of 1873 differences were ironed out, and by midsummer boundary marking had begun in earnest.

The list of George's duties ran to many pages. In essence, the Canadian government wanted him to find out all he could about the natural resources of the areas along the 49th Parallel, with a view to future settlement. He was to suggest the best means of overcoming obstacles to settlement. He was asked to collect any new and important facts of scientific value, to search and assay the value of veins and lodes of useful minerals, and to examine and test soils; and also to find if there were materials useful for building houses. He was to discover and mark on his maps sources of water supply in arid districts. He was to make a careful examination of the completely unknown region surrounding the Lake of the Woods. Everywhere he was to study and report on plant and animal life as it might apply to the productiveness of the country.

He wasted no time in getting his gear together. What should a man take with him for such an expedition? He needed tents and axes and rifles; buckets and pans and a teapot; three horses and a wagon and a Red River cart; horseshoes and sails and a saddle; plant presses, boards and paper and ink; a barometer, a telescope and a compass; specimen boxes and bottles and collecting jars; a geologist's hammer and some collecting bags; four mousetraps; and two wooden chests for bird and animal skins.

He took, as well, his photographic equipment, including a black, light-proof tent, and chemicals for processing his film. He was to be one of the first geological surveyors to use a camera as part of his scientific equipment; the vision he had had long before, during the years of his convalescence, was about to become a reality.

The family buried their own misgivings in the face of George's happiness, and did all they could to help him get ready. In mid-August the final day came. They all went down to Windsor Station to wave good-bye. With puffing and snorting and clanging of bells, the train chugged slowly off and entered the great iron tube called Victoria Bridge which spanned the St. Lawrence River.

It was necessary for George to travel part of the way by train through the United States, and then by stagecoach and horseback to Dufferin at Lake of the Woods. It was the end of the month before he rode into the base camp of the British Boundary Commission.

N.W.T.

YUKON

Dawson City

Pelly River

Queen Charlotte Islands

Wrangell

Portage Lake

STIKINE River

Liard River

BRITISH COLUMBIA

ALBERTA

SASKATCHEWAN

Saskatchewan River

MANITOBA

Milk River

Brandon

Ft. Garry

Lake of the Woods

Dufferin Pembina

Red River

Ft. Frances

ONTARIO

Lake Superior

73

7
Skookum
Tumtum

Immediately upon his arrival at Dufferin, George began his first job: the examination of the regions surrounding the Lake of the Woods. This was a dangerous and almost unknown area, but it had long ago been reported that warring Indians had a secret route across the lake and along rivers to a point near Fort Garry. The Canadian government wanted to find out if it would be feasible to improve this trail so that it could be used as a safe short-cut for settlers in the west. George was also commissioned to find out if there might be mineral deposits or good farmland along the way.

Sixteen years before, a British expedition, headed by John Palliser, had attempted to locate the trail and make a report but they had been stopped at Fort Frances, on Rainy River, by a delegation of two hundred Ojibwas. The Ojibwas had marched threateningly into the fort, faces painted, wearing beaded headdresses bedecked with eagle feathers, and fully armed. They had warned the expedition not to enter their territory. After the Chief and Palliser had exchanged many long speeches, the Indians had been pacified with promises and with gifts of tobacco and firearms.

74

Palliser and his men had eventually found their way through to Red River and Lower Fort Garry.

They had reported that the area was "neither all water nor all land," and that no road or waterway could be built across the muskeg except at enormous expense.

That expedition (1857-1860) had pushed on across the prairies and into the Rocky Mountains in the same direction the Boundary Commission would take. Unlike the men of the Commission, who had to follow an imaginary line, Palliser's men had been able to choose their way, journeying by horseback, canoe, raft or Red River cart in summer, and by snowshoe and dog team in winter—taking whatever seemed the easiest route. When Palliser and his men had returned they had told exciting stories about buffalo hunts, fights with grizzly bears and encounters with warlike Indian tribes—Blackfeet, Bloods, Piegans and Sarcees. However, some of Palliser's reports had later been proved inaccurate, and had therefore not been studied seriously before being shelved.

It was up to George to verify or disprove the earlier findings. It was just the kind of challenge he liked—the chance of success against great odds. His expedition consisted of two men besides himself, a half-breed servant named Begg and a Cree Indian named Spearman who was to act as guide. For conveyance they had one canoe.

On the morning of the dark, windy day when George was ready to push off from Buffalo Bay on Lake of the Woods, the Indian and the half-breed started arguing heatedly in the Swampy Cree dialect. George had not yet learned the language and he grew curious and very impatient.

75

"What's the matter, Begg?" he asked, finally.

"Spearman don't want to go on. He want to go back to Nort'west Angle," Begg told him.

"What's the matter? Is he ill?"

Begg slid one hand under his fur cap to scratch his head.

"No. He's lazy-scared."

"What's he afraid of?" George demanded.

Begg looked down at his tiny boss.

"He's afraid of the Little Doctor."

George's blue eyes widened. He couldn't imagine why the Indian should fear him.

"He's afraid of me! But why?"

"Reed River is plenty bad place. Muskeg Portage very swampy. Injun say we must carry Little Doctor. You too small, too weak."

George's face flushed with anger. The old need to prove he was stronger than the rest rose fiercely in him.

"You tell Spearman that if he has to carry me I'll make him a present of this canoe, and all the gear that's in it. Now, let's go!"

Begg laughed and translated. The Indian shook his head and grumbled, but he stepped into the heavily-laden canoe. It was a bleak, cloudy morning, and a strong wind blew across the lake, making white caps on the tossing waves. The two paddlers worked steadily. The sky grew darker, and the waves rose higher, and, as the weather grew worse, Begg looked back at George with a question in his eyes.

George signalled him to go on.

If he had had more experience in the wilderness, or hadn't been so angry, he wouldn't have braved such a sea. But by the time he realized their very real danger, it was

76

too late to go back. The short, high, choppy waves of the shallow lake were more dangerous to the canoe than the great rolling seas of the Atlantic had been to the *Lake Erie*. George knew now why Spearman had carefully tied a tin mug to one of the thwarts with strong twine just before they pushed off. At a signal from Begg, he began to bail water from the bottom of the craft. He worked furiously, knowing that at any moment the canoe could be swamped. What a fool he had been! Why hadn't he accepted the obvious suggestion in Begg's eyes? He was a greenhorn in the wilderness, and these men had grown up handling canoes and knew these treacherous waters. From now on—if they weren't all drowned—he would listen to what they had to say.

Drenched to the skin, George bailed and bailed. By the time they reached the shelter of the mouth of Reed River, he was acutely aware that only the great skill of the paddlers had saved their lives.

"We made it, Doctor. Look back!" gasped Begg, his chest heaving from exertion, his dark face dripping.

George looked with awe at the white surf thundering on the wild, deserted shore. The wind shrieked through the tossing limbs of the poplar trees and flattened the rushes that grew everywhere in that marshy region. He turned to Begg.

"Yes, we made it, thanks to you," he admitted, which was the nearest he could come to an apology. He felt an unfamiliar sting of shame. If these men had drowned it would have been his fault. A leader should never make such a mistake.

Suddenly he was shivering.

"We'll stop for tea before we go up the river," he said.

The other two exchanged glances. George preferred not to know what they were thinking.

The rain stopped and the wind died while they were taking their refreshments, and they were able to put on some dry clothes before starting out again, but paddling up Reed River proved to be almost as difficult as fighting the waves on the lake. The current was strong and swift at the mouth, then the river turned and twisted in its bed, and ended at last in a dismal, treeless area covered by such tall reeds there was no telling where the swamp ended and the land began. Here they had to make camp for the night.

That evening they hovered close to their smudge fire in a vain effort to escape the hordes of mosquitoes.

Begg grinned as George slapped and scratched and choked and coughed in the smoke.

"You know where mosquitoes come from?" he asked.

"They must be the work of the Devil!" exclaimed George.

"You think so? I heard it another way. Once Cree Indians had a great famine. Many died, until one day two hunters, after long prayer, killed a white wolverine. White wolverine very rare. An old woman jumped out of the skin. She was Manitou. She promised much food if the Indians would take her home and give her the choice from each kill. All was well. But the people got tired of seeing the old woman eat the best meat. They killed her. Then they were afraid. They moved far away. They forgot the old woman. Long after, the tribe came again to the same place. They saw the skeleton. One man laughed. He kicked the skull. Smoke came from the eyes and ears. The smoke was a cloud of insects. They attacked the hunters. The men ran to the river and jumped in. More and more smoke poured from the skull. Now all the land is full of mosquitoes."

George was delighted by the story and the fluent way Begg told it. He had never heard or thought about the stories and beliefs of the Indians before. This was the first of many wonderful stories he was to hear sitting around a campfire at night.

The mosquitoes hummed about his head, swarming into his eyes, his nose, his ears. The bottle of evil-smelling, sticky stuff Anna had concocted for him didn't help. Various remedies had been suggested before he left Montreal— mixtures of pennyroyal and almond oil, or oil of tar and turpentine. At the base camp the men had said the only thing that would give any real protection was an evil ointment made of equal parts of tar and pork fat, but he doubted whether any of these mixtures were better than Anna's remedy.

Long after his guides were asleep, George sat piling bits of dried grasses on the smoldering heap, listening to the hum of the billions of insects, and the deep-throated croaking of bullfrogs hidden in the sedges. Suddenly, grinning to himself, he got out notebook and pencil and began to scribble some lines by the uncertain light of the flickering flames.

> There is a haunting presence everywhere,
> The air is full of music and song,
> Oh, smudge! Oh glorious smudge! Let me
>   entrench in thy sweet noxious cloud
> And nose and eyes all smarting with thy
>   stench, there curse the winged crowd!

He tucked his notebook away. Now there came the lonely howl of a timber wolf, followed by an answering chorus. The calls, eerily musical and varying in length and sound, were repeated again and again. George recognized, with a sense of wonder, that the wolves were exchanging messages. Perhaps they were telegraphing the news that strange men had invaded their territory.

Overhead, the distant stars twinkled steadfastly, arranged in their familiar patterns. The air was pungent with marshy odours mingled with the smoke from his grass fire.

He crawled under his netting. Spearman grunted in his sleep. George wondered what strange dream troubled him. He decided he liked this Indian, who was sensitive as any wild creature to the smells and sights and sounds of the wilderness. He thought he would like to know more about Indians, what they thought about the universe, and what they talked about among themselves. If he could learn their language and win their confidence, they could teach him many things.

He was just dozing off when there was a sudden rustling in the tall reeds. He sat up and listened intently.

Hostile Ojibwas?

A sudden splash, and a silvery ripple in the water betrayed the presence of a muskrat. George smiled at his own nervousness, and settled himself at last to sleep.

The following day the three travellers reached the source of the Reed River where they had to look for the beginnings of Muskeg Portage, which Palliser had found and reported. The river had grown smaller and more sluggish until it disappeared altogether among the rushes of the swamp. Finally the canoe drifted to a stop.

No one spoke, but George knew the Indian was baffled. If they could not find the way through here, they would have to turn back. His heart sank. All the time they had been travelling he had been making notes and sketches of his observations. He had hoped to make a far better report than Palliser, and to define the Indian route clearly with maps and charts. Now he felt a bitter sense of failure. If Spearman couldn't find the path, there was no choice but to give up. Time was precious, since he was already late joining the staff of the Boundary Commission, and the camps had to keep moving ahead. It was necessary for him to move with them.

Suddenly Spearman grunted, and pointed ahead. At first George could see nothing except an unbroken line of tall swaying rushes, but as they approached slowly he saw that a threadlike track led through the reeds, where the water was too shallow and the way too narrow for paddling even the smallest craft.

The men got out and began to drag the canoe after them along a narrow rut worn deep by the hauling of other canoes. At first George couldn't help glancing about anxiously. He was always aware that hostile Ojibwas might be lurking nearby. The swamp was alive with noises: the harsh quacking of ducks, the croaking of frogs, the soughing of the wind through the tall sedges. But the other men were absorbed in their work and soon George himself had to devote all his energies to slogging along the muddy trail.

The water became more and more shallow, until, at last, the canoe ran aground. Now Spearman indicated that each man should take out as much as he could carry. George's load was as heavy as any, and he carried it easily for several hundred yards. Here the water was deeper, so they put their loads on a big, half-submerged rock and went back for the canoe.

Now they were in the swamp basin proper, where the going was even tougher. Spearman and Begg tied themselves by ropes to the thwarts of the canoe and pulled it behind them, like horses harnessed to a sledge. George followed behind, and pushed whenever they came to a particularly bad place. He had made one bad mistake. He had worn a pair of long moccasins. Water seeped in over the tops, and he was soon lifting a quart of it with each step. Squish, squelch, slosh, squish, squelch, slosh—he counted his steps and dragged his heavy feet.

He decided one of the first things he had to learn about muskeg country was how to dress. From now on, he was going to watch closely and imitate his Indian companions. He was miserably uncomfortable, and soon exhausted. He dropped behind. Finally he gave up, and looked around for a place to rest. Here and there solid hummocks protruded above the surface of the swamp. He perched himself on one, pulled off his moccasins, and emptied out the water. He opened his packsack, but the only footwear he could find was a pair of woollen stockings. He pulled those on, tied them tightly at the ankles with string so that the deep oozy mud would not suck them off, and stepped back into the swamp. Now he moved more quickly and soon caught up with the others. Spearman greeted him with a sour look. George grinned. He guessed that already the Indian had been hoping to take possession of his canoe.

They struggled on. It was no longer swamp, but true muskeg, covered with wiry grass and moss, so that often it was hard to tell what was land and what was water. (Much of the great barren lands of Canada's sub-Arctic are muskeg, which freezes solid during the long winter months and provides a solid footing for wandering caribou and Indians and Eskimos, but which is practically impassable in midsummer.) Here and there clumps of spindly tamaracks huddled together in dismal-looking groves.

The water through which the men pulled the canoe was often knee-deep, and now and then George plunged in up to his waist. He was thankful that the day was warm, and that they were sheltered from the wind. But he was amazed at his own stamina.

It was an unbelievable place. Sometimes the muskeg, when he stepped on it, seemed to move and quake for ten feet all around. George would make his way over to a patch of what looked like solid ground, but as soon as he stepped on it, the earth would sink with a hissing sound, and streams of choking, sulphurous gas squirted into the air. Surely no human being had ever ventured into a more vile region! It made him think of the horrible dreams his grandfather had once evoked with his vivid descriptions of hell. To add to the unreality of the weird scene, there were hundreds of small fishes poking about among the grasses. Fish out of water!

Muddy, gasping for breath, plagued by insects, without any real sense of time or place, not for a moment did George think of giving up the exploration. Neither Begg nor Spearman uttered a word of complaint. Dressed partly in buckskins, and partly in the cast-off rags of white men, they were still true sons of the wilderness. Well, thought George, if they could go through muskeg, he could too. It was his business to find out what the territory was like—good or bad.

About noon he accepted Begg's suggestion that it would be wise to rest, and called a halt for tea. He stopped beside a tussock of grass which stood higher than the surrounding ground.

"This will have to serve as stove and banquet table," he announced.

The men sloshed about, gathering dead tamarack twigs, and in a short time the fire was crackling merrily and the pot of water, slung from a stick, began to steam. George threw in a handful of precious black tea leaves. They stood knee-deep in water while they sipped the hot, aromatic drink and munched on hard biscuits.

George laughed.

"I'd like to have a picture of this."

He had a sudden recollection of his mother's worried last instructions. "Now do remember George! You must never stand around with damp feet."

His perspiring, mud-covered companions stared at him in puzzlement. They didn't see anything funny at all.

There wasn't much to laugh at during the rest of that long day. The whole world became an endless stretch of treacherous, stinking muskeg. George's stockinged feet turned into leaden lumps of mud. He lifted them up and put them down again: up and down, over and over interminably. He thought of little besides the next step. When at last they came out to a great open grassy place and saw the woods far off, George gave a shout of joy. The men looked at him and grinned. They still had a long way to go, and all of them were exhausted. Frequent rests became

84

necessary and it was dusk before they found a little rivulet rushing out of the swamp and could float the canoe again. This was what they had been looking for. It was the source of the Rousseau River and from then on the route would be easy to follow. The first battle had been won.

The weary men threw themselves down on the ground in a poplar grove. The soil was damp and spongy. There was no place to pitch a tent and they were too tired to make a meal. Luckily the night was warm and George awoke next day refreshed and with a sense of accomplishment.

But the triumph was short-lived. They soon found that the Rousseau River presented another problem: it proved unnavigable even for a canoe. Over and over again the travellers were stopped by beaver dams or windfalls. It might be good fur-trapping country but the trail would need many improvements before it could ever serve as a transport route for the settlers on their way to the Red River. In this, Palliser had been quite correct.

At the end of the Rousseau River they came out again into a vast treeless swamp. Firewood had to be chopped and gathered and loaded into the canoe before they dared to go any farther.

That night they slept again in the open, on a mud bank. Before morning they were awakened by a cold rain beating on their faces and the sound of wind whistling across the swamp. They got up and crawled under the over-turned canoe and huddled together until the storm was over. It was two o'clock in the afternoon before they found dry land and built a good fire.

George had tried his luck at bringing down a few of the birds that abounded in the marshes. He prided himself on his marksmanship, and was eager to demonstrate his ability, but he had only empty cartridges to show for his efforts. Shooting waterfowl from a canoe, he discovered, was quite different from firing at a target on land. One had to allow for the slightest movement of a light craft floating on still water and then, as Begg explained, one had to estimate how fast the bird was flying, and to aim ahead of it. George tried again and again before he gave up. He marvelled a bit enviously at the ease with which Begg brought down three ducks in rapid succession.

What a mouth-watering, delicious aroma filled the nostrils of the hungry men! The ducks slowly turned a golden brown as they roasted on sticks over the hot coals and when at last they were done, George thought that never in all his life had he tasted anything so good. After the meal, he passed around tobacco. It was pure bliss to be warm and dry and well fed. He had never been so at peace with himself and with the world.

After a while Spearman said something in Cree to Begg, which made the half-breed glance at George and laugh.

"What's the joke?" George asked lazily.

"Spearman say you *skookum tumtum*."

"What's that?"

Begg scratched his lank black hair, trying to think of words to translate the Indian expression into English.

"It means you strong, tough man, and it means you brave, cheery man. You laugh when things go bad. Spearman say you keep canoe. If you need guide another day, Spearman come."

George felt a thrill of deep pleasure. Such praise from an Indian was a rare thing. He didn't know it then, but the name Skookum Tumtum was going to travel ahead of him wherever he went in the wilderness. The Little Doctor was a good man—*skookum tumtum.*

8
Boundary
Commission

Skookum Tumtum was rather like a name earned in an initiation rite, and quite possibly George thought of it in that way. In any case, when he settled to his work on the Commission, he had a deep respect for his Indian guide and a determination to become a true woodsman—alert to every sight, sound and smell of the world about him.

Although he was now in the company of several hundred men, the going was not easy. No civilized man lived along the rough path that the members of the Boundary Commission had to mark out—1200 miles in an undeviating straight line. They had to penetrate thick forests, build bridges over swamps and rivers, cross the dry prairies and deeply gullied, arid badlands. Most boundaries are comparatively easy to mark because they follow natural geographical lines, such as the course of a river, or the border of a lake, but this is not possible when a parallel of latitude is chosen. In this case the line is drawn on a map, and the boundary must be located on site by making astronomical observations. For the 49th Parallel boundary the chief astronomers and their staffs—Lieutenant Colonel Francis U. Farquhar for the United States, and Lieutenant Samuel Anderson for Canada—had to move ahead of the surveyors to show where the markers should be placed.

Behind them, a caravan of covered wagons moved slowly across the plains in a great cloud of yellow dust, making an average of about twenty miles a day. The shouts of the drivers, the cracks of the whips, the braying of the mules were usually drowned by the creaking, groaning, screeching noise of the Red River carts. (To avoid clogging the wheels with dust and dirt, no grease was used on the axles. And if a wooden wheel or shaft was broken it was mended on the spot with wet strips of buffalo hide. As it dried, the hide shrank and hardened, which, though it made the wheel tough, and long-lasting, also made it noisy.)

At night the carts and wagons were drawn up in a semicircular corral near a source of water, and the tents pitched outside the wagons. The horses, for protection against Indian theft, were tethered at dusk inside the corral.

To mark the boundary in treed areas, posts were placed at three-mile intervals. On the open prairie, where posts were not available, earthen mounds were built. (These were temporary markers; in 1909 and 1912 they were replaced at closer intervals by permanent cast-iron monuments.)

No defences were erected along the way. Canada and the United States were friendly nations, and the boundary between them is the longest undefended international boundary in the world.

There were twelve *official* members of each branch of the Commission but hundreds of other men were also employed, and for two successive summers—1873, 1874—the cavalcades of the Commission moved like armies across the middle of the North American continent. The Americans preferred mule teams to pull their covered wagons. The British chose mostly oxen. Because of Indian uprisings in their country, the Americans were protected by two companies of regular cavalry and a company of infantry—about 230 men; the British had only an irregular guard of thirty men, mostly Métis, who acted as guides and as hunters for meat.

The Métis, descendants of the seventeenth-century French voyageurs or the Scottish factors who had married Indian wives had, in two hundred years, developed into a proud race, neither Indian nor white, and accepted by neither race. As wild and free as the buffalo, they wandered back and forth across the open prairies. Their life depended on the buffalo and on being able to follow the herds, and they had looked with fierce hostility at the first surveyors who had come with measuring chains to divide the land into square lots and take it as their own, without even asking to whom it belonged. In time they had come to hate and distrust white men, and under Louis Riel they were still, in 1873, making a great deal of trouble.

The Métis who hired themselves out to the British Boundary Commission must have been outlaws from their own band. But they knew the prairie like no others, and were magnificent scouts. The British, though wary of them, were glad to have them, and George Dawson had no trouble with them at all.

As a matter of fact, George had little or no trouble with full-blooded Indians either. It is possible that his strange appearance was a kind of passport into Indian territory, for the Indians revered anyone out of the ordinary. Certainly

90

his reputation as Skookum Tumtum went ahead of him wherever he went.

George covered hundreds of more miles in his work than the men employed in the actual boundary marking, making side-trips from every base camp, northward into Canadian territory, observing the geological formation of the land, trapping specimens of birds and animals, many of them new and strange to the outside world, taking temperatures, measuring humidity, testing soils for content and fertility, collecting mosses, wild flowers, grasses, insects and fossils— anything that could add to his knowledge of the country.

The most interesting discovery he made, by far, was at Wood Mountain, near the present-day village of Killdeer, about half-way across Saskatchewan. He was digging in stratified shale about six miles from the base when he found fragments of enormous fossilized bones, unlike any he had ever seen before. There was only time to collect a few of the bones, as the discovery was made near the end of the first season, but he took what he could. It was later learned that some of them were those of a hadrosaurian dinosaur and some were bones of ancient turtles. The pieces that he and his helpers collected proved to be the first dis- covered in a place that has since become one of the richest hunting grounds for dinosaur fossils in the world.

George often went off by himself, even though he knew it was a dangerous thing to do. If something caught his in- terest, he was off like a hunting dog on a scent. He had the reputation of being absolutely fearless.

Although George was never troubled by the Indians, the camp was. Once when he returned to West Butte he found everything in confusion.

91

"What's happened?" he asked Dr. Burgess.

"We've been robbed. Indians," said the doctor.

"Has anybody been hurt?"

"No, nothing as bad as that. But we've lost all our tea and sugar and nearly all our matches—and many other things besides. That's what comes of carelessness. Only three men were left on guard today."

George whistled softly in shocked disapproval.

"Well, we can live without tea or sugar, I suppose. But matches . . . hmmm. Someone will need to keep a fire going."

Dr. Burgess shrugged.

"We have plenty of rawhide whips and lariats, anyway. The Indians, a party of four hundred Piegans, took what they wanted in a very friendly manner, and left a great pile of these useless things in exchange."

George laughed.

Dr. Burgess looked down at him in surprise.

"You're the only one who's found it funny," he said.

The Americans had no geologist in their party. Dr. Elliot Coues, their medical officer, was also their naturalist, but his knowledge in this area lay chiefly with zoology.

The British had two medical men, Dr. Burgess and Dr. Millman, but they didn't have much doctoring to do, as the men remained remarkably healthy. Dr. Burgess shared a tent with George, and George couldn't stand to see anyone idle. He soon had both Burgess and Millman working long hours for him. In his report, he gives special thanks to these men, who collected and helped to identify hundreds of the most interesting plants listed.

George's enthusiasm was contagious, and soon even some of the military personnel joined in the work of collecting. Thomas Duckworth was pressed into service as taxidermist, and George reported that he proved "very useful and zealous."

Anyone who offered to help Dawson, however, had to work carefully and follow his instructions implicitly. He was a perfectionist and a hard taskmaster. He rejected anything second-rate out of hand, but if a man brought in a particularly fine specimen he would pause in whatever he was doing to exclaim, "Oh, isn't that a beauty!" And the man would feel amply repaid for his pains.

The truth was that George was beginning to lose himself in his work. He had learned the knack of total concentration, of becoming oblivious to everything except the business at hand. Some said of him that he was a kind of machine, impervious to the worst weather, able to subsist all day without food or water. Unfortunately he often forgot that other men were not as tough and not as dedicated as himself.

All that summer he kept his usual detailed records and wrote his weekly letters to Anna. His letters were often brief and brisk now, and dealt chiefly with his work, so that Anna complained that he no longer said anything about himself. George wrote back:

You say my letters merely relate to facts and don't say anything as to what I am thinking about, and I suppose this is true, but really I think travelling about over the plains does not conduce to much thought, one's chief thought is to get warm and something to eat, which having been accomplished you feel sleepy and so wrap yourself up in your blanket and go to sleep . . . . Having once worked out a train of thought about a buffalo skull, a burnt prairie, an unburnt prairie, a tuft of grass, a prairie chicken; one has to begin and go over the list again—or to go along without thinking at all.

On 5 November, George wrote again to Anna in the same vein from Dufferin:

Nearly all the prairie along the line is burned and for a picture of desolation I don't think burnt prairie partially covered with snow can well be surpassed. There was of course no grass for the horses, and what with very little hay and very little oats, many of them played out, and several carts and animals were left behind.

When camped in one place with plenty of wood at hand and a stove in a tent, one may be moderately comfortable even in such weather, but on the move every day and all day long, with neither of these advantages and often obliged to camp after dark, things become mixed. Bread or beef or ink and everything freezable being frozen is not conducive to comfort—and getting up in the morning before daybreak with the thermometer far far below the freezing point is unpleasant. One night the temperature fell well below zero. However, all went well, and the whole of the men are now back without accident of any kind.

Parties coming in would have given good opportunity to some caricaturist fond of motley groups, all sorts of makeshifts and rigups being the order of the day. Some men with torn clothes, others with gaping boots, some with blanket suits and some with none at all, mackintoshes below coats and head pieces that had seen a summer of wear . . . .

But George's sense of humour still prevailed and he ended his letter with a poem.

HAT

Roof of the forge and working house of thought
Thou shield from sol's fierce rays
Far through the forest by hard scratching brought
And many devious ways—
Thou summer rag at best, I have thee here
A prey to autumn and to winter wind
The days are chill, the snows are almost here—
While I go southward to a land less drear
A new felt tile must cover up my mind!

G.M.D.

By Christmas he was back in Montreal, busier than ever. His father attended the opening of the boxes of specimens with the same anticipation and delight of discovery that George had experienced as a small boy in Pictou, when his father would come home from one of *his* expeditions.

Many specialists were now working at McGill, and all were eager to help with the sorting. Besides his father, who took over the identification of fossil plants, there was his eccentric old friend, Dr. Carpenter, the expert on shells. Professor Cope gave valuable assistance in identifying vertebrate fossils—such as the hadrasaurian dinosaur bones—and a Mr. Scudden (mentioned in George's report) was an expert on insects. A group of botanists worked with the collections of grasses, mosses and flowering plants. Often in the past George had worked with most of these men. Now the roles were reversed.

Winter passed and with spring George went west again. The second season was almost as remarkable for its voyage west as for anything discovered on the job. The trip was made by train via Chicago as far as Morehead in Minnesota. The rest of the way to the base camp at Dufferin George had to go by stage. Although in late March and early April it was still bitterly cold, George sat outside on the box beside the driver whenever possible, studying the contours of the land, watching for willow catkins or swelling buds on poplar or maple trees, listening for bird calls —always ready to record anything of interest.

The road was so bad that the driver—as drivers often did—took his coach across the prairie, running the risk of getting lost in a blizzard, or falling through a deceptive patch of snow or thin ice into a flooded coulee. These deep hollows were traps into which horses could plunge and coaches become hopelessly mired. In addition to those dangers it was risky to ride outside, because if the coach struck a frozen hummock one could be flung off—as George was on this trip.

"I don't know which part of my anatomy hit the ground first," he told Anna afterwards. "But judging from the condition of my hat, it must have been my head."

A little farther on, the driver of the same stage got lost. He pulled up on the brink of a swift-flowing river.

"Buffalo Creek," he announced to George. "There's supposed to be a new bridge and the inn's just before we get there—but danged if I know where 'tis."

Alarmed, George saw that already it was getting dark.

"Isn't that a light toward the southwest?"

The driver peered through the gloom.

"Danged if it ain't. You got the sharpest eyes on you of any feller I know," he said.

The light shone from the window of a log cabin, and the settler told them how to find the bridge. On the hill that led down to the bridge, however, the horses plunged into a half-thawed drift and couldn't get out. Passengers had to alight and make their way, as well as they could, in the darkness and cold, slogging through ankle-deep mud until they arrived at the inn, leaving the driver to free the horses as best he could.

Next morning they found the only way to get across Red River was to walk part way on ice, then cross the open water in rowboats. An ancient coach on the other side had to be repaired before they could proceed.

Finally they got on their way, but they had nothing to eat from breakfast until seven at night, when they arrived at Goose River. Here the meal consisted of bread, fried fat pork and potatoes, with doughnuts for dessert. George, writing home, said that all meals at stage stops were much the same: "The whole spread has a greasy appearance, and the remains of eggs of two or three seasons may be detected on close examination sticking between the iron prongs of the forks."

Often the only bed to be had for his bruised and aching body was a dirty blanket on a hard floor.

After such a trip, the accommodation in the barracks at

Dufferin seemed luxurious. But life became monotonous there after a few weeks of waiting and everyone was glad when they pushed on again to the last camp established the year before.

On 31 July, George wrote home from Three Buttes:

Here we are camped at the western end of the west butte of the three, with the Rocky Mountains in sight. The Rockies are about 115 miles distant, and on a clear day are beautifully defined and show great white patches either of snow or some light coloured rock. I move on again tomorrow. . . .

Ashe, who is doing the survey work now, came in last night with the report that, in running a survey line, he had come across twenty-one dead Indians . . . probably a party of Crows who had left the country near Fort Benton last autumn on a horse stealing expedition, had been surprised by an over-whelming number of Piegans, and had never returned . . . . It was decided to send the photographers.

I thought I could not do better than go too, and have only now returned from the trip. The spot was about ten miles from here on the open undulating prairie. The remains were in quite a mummified state, the skin being tightly stretched over the bones, and the latter only protruding where the wolves, etc. had been depredating, and where the scalps had been removed from the forehead to the back of the neck . . . .

The story of the fight was pretty plain. The Crows, if such they were, had evidently been on foot, and their adversaries mounted. The Crows, on finding themselves surrounded, had chosen a sloping hill and probably choosing badger holes already dry, had enlarged them and piled stones around the edge so as to form shallow rifle pits. Their enemies had no doubt ridden round and round at full speed, firing at them as they rode in Indian style, and finally succeeded in killing the whole party. The Crows had shot one of the horses, and probably some of the men, but these had probably been removed . . . . The skulls were all destroyed by being broken in and the bodies had evidently been cut and slashed in all directions after death. We picked up some arrow heads, the chamber of a revolver, a few beads and an old knife . . . .

These buttes and the line of the Milk River bound a sort of neutral ground between four or five tribes of Indians, and these Indians never pass except in war parties. This accounts for their absence at present, and for the fact that no recent campfires or lately-killed buffalo are seen in this part of the country.

That discovery—and the Rocky Mountains—were probably the most remarkable events in George's second year with the Commission.

George had found his work on the prairies fascinating and rewarding, but he did not know what it was to fall in love with the land until he caught his first glimpse of the Rocky Mountains. When he reached the foothills, he pushed on alone to climb his first peak. And when he gazed from that summit, with awe at the grandeur spread above and around and below him, he knew that his heart had been stolen forever. On his way down he picked a single forget-me-not and sent it to Anna. And he wrote a poem beginning, "God's peace upon the mountain land . . . ." All his life George had that feeling about the mountains. Once he said, "I feel as if the mountains belong to me."

By mid-October the last marker had been placed, and George was back in Dufferin. But he made a vow that he would return to the West as soon as it was humanly possible.

9
Geological Survey

In his mind as well as in his notes, George had begun to organize his report almost as soon as he'd begun to gather specimens. It was easy for him to arrange things in a pattern, perhaps because he had always liked to draw and paint pictures and write poetry. His mind was as orderly and retentive as a filing cabinet. He wanted his report to be so complete that geologists, and others who came after him, would be able to take over where he left off, and not have to begin all over again, or be left with large gaps to fill. He believed that such a report should be of general use—not just to geologists, but to prospectors, miners, farmers, even to engineers when they started to build the great railroad that Prime Minister Sir John A. Macdonald was always talking about.

Most such reports consist chiefly of dry statistics and make for dull reading, but *The Dawson Report on the Geology and Resources of the Region in the Vicinity of the 49th Parallel* is an exception. It is as descriptive as it is informative. In his first notes about Lake of the Woods, for example, he said:

The greater part of the southern and western margin

is . . . utterly useless and a more forbidding and deso-
late region can scarcely be imagined . . . . In some
places low swampy savannah fronts directly on the
lake and this I have seen fringed after a gale by a belt
many feet in width of brown vegetable pulp . . . im-
possible to walk on, impassable for a canoe . . . .

But George found something of value even in this deso-
late region. "Wild, or Indian rice must grow luxuriantly in
northern divisions . . . where Indians collect large quantities for winter use," he wrote, and suggested that wild rice
could become an important crop in those swampy areas
which were unsuited for other crops.

He praised the climate: ". . . the shallow expanse of water becomes heated by the rays of the sun and the nights
are here deliciously balmy . . . ."

The area surrounding Lake of the Woods remains today
much as George found it. Although wild rice has never become an important crop and his description of this area is
perhaps the least noteworthy part of his report, his account
contained all the valuable data he had collected about the
formation of vast stretches of prairie land, and served many
an explorer and settler with sound advice. The book contains a wealth of information on geology, mineral resources,
climate, agricultural possibilities, rainfall, evaporation, naturally occurring plants, the birds and animals native to the
region, and many detailed and systematic observations
which proved to be almost as useful south of the newly-
marked border as in Canada. It is still used as a textbook
today by students of Canadian geology.

The report points out that the inhabitants of the semi-
arid regions of the interior plains should be taught to re-

102

frain from setting wild grass fires. "... the most trivial signal of one Indian to another has often cost hundreds of acres of forest tree ... often starvation and misery to Indians themselves ... driving the animals from their retreats, and marring the fair face of nature ...." Such fires were the scourge of the prairies, as George had learned from personal experience, for more than once he had almost lost his life as the result of one. An account in the diary he kept in the Boundary Commission years, in its curt description tells how devastating prairie fire could be.

Monday 20 October 1873: Prairie fire raging not far off on both sides of creek. Hastened departure that it might not overtake us in the long grass of the bottom. After travelling about two miles found the fire rapidly coming up behind us, urged by a strong west wind which bore volumes of smoke and ashes. Found it necessary to fire the prairie and remain on the burnt patch till the main fire had passed ahead. This it did with amazing rapidity and we travelled the whole way to depot over black burnt ground which half an hour before had been covered with thick prairie grass. Fire raging in bushes and grass of river valley all round the depot and kept in anxiety some time by it.

The Report on the Geology and Resources of the Region in the Vicinity of the 49th Parallel is "phenomenally complete and accurate," says Dr. A. H. Lang, a retired member of the Geological Survey of Canada. George Dawson seemed to possess an uncanny seventh sense which enabled him, according to Dr. Lang, not only to make thorough and valid observations quickly, but to extend such observations to distant vistas in a way that has never been equalled. In a pamphlet on George Dawson, Dr. Lang writes:

The study of western coals was begun by Richardson and Selwyn. . . . It was advanced greatly by Dawson because of his superior training and intellect, the much greater territory covered by him, and the much longer time he worked in the west. The Boundary Report contains details for numerous seams of low-grade coal of the lignite variety in what is now Manitoba and Saskatchewan, which he considered suitable for local heating and industrial purposes.

The chapter on fuel supplies in Macoun's *Manitoba and the Great North West* is virtually a series of quotations from the Boundary Report. Dawson showed that large deposits of coal of better qualities underlay much of the Alberta plains, that especially good steam coal occurred in quantity in the mountains not far from Banff, and that much coking coal was present in the Crow's Nest area. He also described many coal deposits in the plateaux and mountains west of the Rockies. Some of his descriptions were so detailed that no further elaboration has ever been required. . . . Later western geologists have tried to imitate his methods, with poorer results.

The report was an instant success—a best-seller among scientists. The first edition sold out within a few months and second-hand copies sold for very high prices.

Prairie fires, hostile Métis, the miseries of stagecoach travel, days of hunger when the only meal was boiled blackbirds, nights when buzzing mosquitoes meant specialized torture, storms that carried off tents or threatened to swamp canoes—memories of such hardships could not keep

104

George at home. They were only a minor part of a great adventure just begun.

For George the success of his report meant one thing above all—the assurance of the career he wanted. In 1875 he received the appointment he had hoped and worked for so long: he became paleontologist to the Geological Survey of Canada. His brave feet were firmly planted on the ladder of success. But before he set forth on another expedition, he kept his promise to Archie Pinchey about filling in the gaps of the Canadian exhibit at the British Museum. Two hundred and ninety-nine specimens of birds, and sixteen specimens of mammals were gratefully accepted by the curator, who wrote, ". . . this contribution to the National Collection has proved to be a very valuable one, filling up a great gap in our series of North American animals—not only are the specimens in an excellent state of preservation, but they were collected with the discernment and knowledge of an experienced collector . . . ."

(Probably George wrote to Pinchey and suggested he go and see the collection, but there is no record of this, or of what became of his good friend of London days.)

That same year George went west again, this time as paleontologist with Dr. A. R. C. Selwyn, then director of the Geological Survey on an expedition to central British Columbia and the Peace River region.

He was George Dawson of the Canadian Geological Survey team and very pleased with himself.

1 Her Majesty's North American Boundary Commission.
   (George Dawson is standing third from right in the back row.)
2 Prairie boundary marker with members of the Commission.
   (This picture and those following were taken by George Dawson.)
3 Close-up of boundary marker

4 Waggon train at Dead Horse Creek near Pembina, Manitoba
5 Side Valley at Milk River, Alberta
6 Boundary Commission encampment

7 Indians building a canoe at Northwest Angle near Lake of the Woods
8 Skeletons of Crow Indians near Three Buttes, Alberta

9 Métis hunters and guides close by their camp near Pembina
10 Indian camp near Pembina
11 George Dawson's camp near West Butte
12 Portion of Dawson's observation tent

10
Summer
with
Rankine

In the summer of 1875 George was asked to do an original survey of the almost unknown Queen Charlotte Islands off the coast of British Columbia. He invited his brother Rankine to go with him.

In those busy years after the Boundary Commission report George had seen almost nothing of his family. In a letter to Anna in December 1875 from Victoria, B.C., he didn't try to hide his loneliness.

> I can hardly believe that it is so near Christmas, the time has slipped away so fast, and here there is no proper winter to mark the time, only a prolonged and dismal autumn, with the vine still clinging to the mouldering wall and the rain and the wind are never weary! The woods are uncommonly full of moss here, for it creeps up the tree trunks and settles in tufts and cushions even on the exposed branches . . . I don't think anything will induce me to spend another winter here, the most out-of-the-way Hudson Bay post on the continent would be preferable . . . .

He was not home either for Anna's wedding to Bernard Harrington the following June. Sophie Brown, one of

110

Anna's friends, wrote him a letter describing the event. She told him that on the day of the wedding the weather was perfect and that the Dawson home had been beautifully decorated with fresh flowers. ". . . Anna looked very well, though rather nervous, and said 'I do' twice instead of once. Old Mrs. Carpenter . . . wept silently, but there was no outcry . . . . Anna wore a beautiful cream-coloured silk which came from Scotland and was trimmed with lace and flowers . . . . On her head she wore a wreath of orange blossoms and jasmine."

Anna wrote of her happiness from Lake George, New York, where she and Bernard were honeymooning, but letters were not visits home, so it was with great delight that George found the opportunity to take Rankine on the Queen Charlotte Islands expedition. Rankine was a medical student at McGill and, though he probably realized that a holiday with George would hardly be restful, he accepted. His brother greeted him warmly at Victoria, where the two waited in a hotel for a schooner to arrive to carry them to the Queen Charlottes.

The big, wedge-shaped islands which comprise a total area of almost four thousand square miles, lie off the coast of northern British Columbia. Mist-shrouded and mysterious, inhabited in 1875 only by small groups of Haida Indians, no one knew anything about the geological formation of the land, whether it was fit for cultivation, or whether any minerals were to be found, or what plants and animals lived in the depths of its forests. The Geological Survey needed to learn these things, and Dr. Dawson had been chosen to do the investigating.

The day which had been set for departure, May 15, came

and went and there was no word from Captain Douglas, owner of the ship which George had hired. Next day, the two brothers found an old schooner, *The Wanderer*, at the dock, and hired her on the spot. Checking her over, George found the sails were rotten. He ordered Captain Sabotson to have the crew replace them. Then, on the morning of the day the ship was to leave Victoria harbour, the young men made another disturbing discovery: Captain Sabotson was drunk.

Rankine was disgusted.

"Now what do we do?"

"We fire the captain. I'll sail her myself," said George cheerfully.

"Oh, no! You can't! I don't care how smart you are! You can't sail a ship through those rough waters. They've never even been charted!"

George puffed on his pipe and looked unconcerned.

"I know something about navigation. Remember my trip on the *Lake Erie* in '69? I haven't forgotten my lessons with the quadrant. We'll get there."

And they did. George, Rankine, and a crew of three set sail from Victoria a few days later. Before the end of May *The Wanderer* cast anchor in the Bay of Skedans before an audience of noisy, cheering Haidas.

People talked about it for years afterward. That little Dr. Dawson, he could do anything. He could even sail a rotten old vessel through the wild waters of the Queen Charlotte Islands right into a harbour where he'd never been before.

It was late afternoon before the crew finished unloading the men and their supplies. George and Rankine set up camp for the night on the beach. Behind them a row of totem poles stood in a semi-circle facing the Bay, guarding the village which lay between them and the towering black forest. The Indians and dogs who had given them such a noisy welcome had mysteriously disappeared. The wind whispered in the pines, the breakers crashed on the shore in white foam, and the eyes in the grotesque carved faces on the poles glared down at them menacingly.

"Spooky, isn't it?" Rankine commented.

George agreed absently. Although sensitively aware of the beauty and mystery of his surroundings, his mind was busy with thoughts of preparations for the exploration of the islands. There was so much to do. And they were so late getting started.

As soon as the tents were up and the equipment under cover, he walked back into the village and found an Indian who could speak some English. He was a fierce looking man, with a hostile look in his eye.

"We need someone who can work for us this summer, to guide us through the forests," George told him.

"Swaawa—cougar—big cat. No one go into forest," he said. George was dumfounded.

"But some of you must be trappers, hunters for meat."

"We don't eat meat. We eat fish."

The smell of fish pervaded the village. George realized unhappily that the statement was probably true. Still, he had to find someone to act as guide. He and Rankine would surely get lost or into serious trouble if they tried to penetrate this unknown northern jungle alone. The Queen Charlotte Islands lay in the coastal rain belt where giant conifers grew to be over two hundred feet high. Approaching the shores in *The Wanderer*, George had observed that even the undergrowth of ferns and scrub and weeds grew higher than a man's head.

The Indian stalked off and as George stood where he was, puzzling over what to do next, Rankine joined him.

"Do you actually know what these people eat, George?" he asked in a low tone. His face was pale and he looked frightened.

"Fish."

"No. Come here. I want to show you something before it gets too dark."

He led the way beyond the village to a huge totem pole. The great mouth was carved open, like the door to a cave, and George could see that the massive pole was hollow.

"Look inside," Rankine commanded.

George looked. The empty eyes of a grinning white human skull stared back at him.

"They're cannibals," Rankine whispered.

George couldn't repress a shiver of revulsion. He said, with greater confidence than he felt, "No, no. I don't believe it. There must be some other explanation. In any case, these totems are sacred, and we'd better not get caught snooping about. Come on, let's get settled for the night."

"Who can sleep?" Rankine demanded.

But finally they did sleep, and in the morning George found several men who were willing to act as guides. Soon the magic of his personal charm took effect, and before many weeks had passed, he had won the confidence of the Haidas and was able to communicate quite freely with them. They knew a little English; he was adept at reading signs; and he could pick up a new language very quickly.

Rankine felt much better about the whole adventure

114

when his brother told him that the giant totem with the skull inside it was a mortuary pole. In such poles the sacred bones of great chiefs were kept.

George was untroubled by the uncivilized habits of the Haidas which disgusted the fastidious Rankine. His genuine interest and respect for the Indians was rewarded. They trusted him with their legends, let him take photographs, and guided him to places where no other white men had ever been. Always he was busy with camera, notebook and pencil.

"This is a most fascinating tribe," he told his brother one evening, when they were back at Skedans.

"Ugh. They smell terrible," said Rankine, who had proved to be a good companion and competent helper in spite of his inexperience and the fact that he was unaccustomed to the hardships of outdoor life.

"They smell a bit fishy," George agreed, "but you must realize that these people are as dependent on fish for all their needs as the Prairie Indians are on the buffalo. They even use fish for candles."

He picked up an oily, dried fish the Haidas called candle-fish, or oolachen. Holding it by its tail, he held the head over a hot coal, and immediately it caught fire. He buried the tail in the sand to hold it upright and watched it burn with a slow, clear flame.

"The oolachen is so important it even figures in the Haidas' story of creation," he said.

"I don't see what an oily fish can have to do with the creation of the universe," said literal-minded Rankine.

"Well, once upon a time . . . ."

"Oh, no! Not another bedtime story!" Rankine groaned.

115

George laughed.

"If you don't want to hear it take a lighted oolachen and go to bed."

"I'll listen," said Rankine, lolling back on the sandy beach, with his hands clasped under his head.

The moon was full and the totem poles behind them cast their weird shadows across the pale sand. The rhythmic sound of the waves lapping the beach was broken suddenly by the harsh scream of a lynx deep in the forest.

"Once upon a time the only light in the heavens was the moon. It belonged to the chief of the Haidas, but one day, when the chief was away on a big fishing trip, the Raven stole the moon and hid it under his wing. Then all the world was in darkness."

George paused, and at that moment a small cloud passed over the face of the moon. Again the lynx screamed. Rankine raised his head on one elbow and looked at the small, gnome-like shape of his brother.

"Don't, George! You're uncanny—creating stage effects with clouds and wild beasts."

George chuckled.

"Oh, well. I'll cut it short. While the world was in darkness, the Haidas had to catch all the oolachen for candles, and the Raven got very hungry. He ate oolachen—that was his diet. So he had to give in. In the end he broke the moon into two pieces, like a cookie. He threw the bigger piece up into the sky for the sun, the smaller piece for the moon, and all the little crumbs he threw up for stars."

"So the Raven traded the sun, moon and the stars for an oily oolachen," said Rankine, disgustedly, getting to his feet. "Good night, George. Don't forget to blow out your fish."

George spent just that one summer on the Queen Charlotte Islands. Study of the Haida Indians could be carried out only when he could spare moments from his geological and geographical tours, on stormy days, or late at night by the light of a campfire. Yet he managed to write a book about them, and even more important, he took photographs of the Indian villages and their totem poles. Soon after his visit the encroachments of the white men destroyed the Haidas' ancient way of life, and few new poles were created. His photographs, along with the unique paintings of the British Columbia artist, Emily Carr, made only a few years later, form a precious record of an almost forgotten art.

From the time of the trip with Begg and Spearman, George had set himself to learn many Indian languages and legends. He had developed a rare understanding of their ways and thinking. He wrote books and pamphlets about various tribes. Because of these studies, in the library of the Geological Survey in Ottawa there is a life-sized portrait of him entitled:

GEORGE MERCER DAWSON
1849-1901
FATHER OF CANADIAN ANTHROPOLOGY

11
Busy
Years

In 1877, as paleontologist, he was asked to work on the mapping of the great coal fields in Alberta. He worked hard on these expeditions and had little time for social life. Furthermore, he wrote little about his personal feelings in his diaries and his letters. He seemed to lead a more and more private life.

There is a family story to the effect that some time in those years, when George was over thirty years old, he fell in love. The parents of the woman he loved opposed the marriage strongly, probably because of George's deformity. She hadn't the courage to brave the disapproval of her family, and married a man they chose for her.

George hid the bitterness of his hurt from the world, but his heart was broken. He relied once again and with great determination on the power of work to keep him from despair. He drove himself very hard, and he drove others hard too.

As long as he was on the trail, pitting his strength against nature, looking for anything that would help to further scientific knowledge or help his country, he could find peace for his lonely spirit. But every winter, when he had to stay for long periods in the city, he became depressed, and only by rigorous self-discipline could he continue to keep a cheerful face to the world. His letters to Anna became shorter and less interesting. But always he was *skookum tumtum*, brave and cheerful.

Not everyone enjoyed working for the Little Doctor. He had absolutely no use for lazy, careless, or indifferent people. He was a perfectionist and he worked at a terrific pace. One young scientist, Joseph Tyrrell, who afterwards became a famous Canadian explorer himself, complained bitterly the first season he worked for Dr. Dawson in 1883.

In May of that year the mapping expedition reached Brandon, Manitoba, which was then the end of the established route from the East. There George bought the necessary equipment, including horses, provisions and tents. After that they crossed the prairies to Maple Creek, where they visited the headquarters of the Royal Canadian Mounted Police.

The officer in charge of the detachment warned them that the way ahead was dangerous, and that they ran the risk of being molested and robbed by outlaws or Indians. Several other small groups had gone into the mountains, and had never been heard from again. Joe Tyrrell was naturally alarmed by this news, and he was dismayed when George laughed, and only promised he would keep a guard to watch his camp.

Joe didn't like his first job in the mountains either. George gave him the work of making a pace survey. That meant walking long distances all alone and measuring the miles by counting the number of steps he took, and then multiplying the average number by the length of his stride.

119

As he trudged along each day, keeping count of his paces by transferring twigs from one pocket to another—each twig representing a hundred steps—Dr. Dawson would sometimes pass him on horseback. Engrossed in his own observations of the terrain, George wouldn't so much as glance at Joe, or ask him how he was getting along.

In the evenings, however, after everyone had eaten, George would light up a cigarette or a pipe, and suddenly become a warm, friendly and congenial companion. He asked Joe about his experiences and looked over his collections. He identified specimens and explained with infinite patience anything Joe wanted to know about his work. Yet he was not interested in the young man's blistered feet, or in his loneliness.

Joe had no way of knowing what George himself had to endure. He really thought that small wiry body must be made of steel and that Dawson had a heart of iron. Yet, all the men were ashamed to complain of hardships to their leader because each of them was big enough to make two of the Little Doctor, and George never asked any man to do anything he wouldn't do himself.

In later life, Joe Tyrrell told all this. He recovered from his youthful bitterness, and he credited Dr. George Dawson with teaching him almost everything of real value he knew.

George loved horses, and was an excellent rider. He took great care of animals (some said he was more thoughtful of the beasts than he was of his men) and as a result, the same animals could be used season after season on his expeditions—a rare thing in those rough days. He had his favourites, and one of his horses, called Major—a sorrel with a long, heavy black tail and mane—used to come into camp every night and nudge his master's pockets, looking for his lump of sugar.

It is easy to understand how a man could love a horse upon whom his very life depended. After all, the faithful animal carried him for hundreds and hundreds of miles through the great empty wilderness. Even tough Sir Francis Butler, who rode west in 1869-70 to help in the protection of the settlers against the Métis, was heartbroken when he lost his Little Blackie. She went through the ice on the prairie, and when he found she was drowning and couldn't be rescued, he was forced to shoot her.

"I went back to the camp, and, sitting down in the snow, cried like a child," he relates.

Daily companionship during an expedition often cemented a warmer friendship between man and horse than that between man and man. A good animal, like Butler's Little Blackie, or Dawson's Major, became expert at detecting and avoiding such dangers as hidden badger holes, which often go straight down three or four feet. If a horse plunged into a hole of that kind it usually meant a broken leg—which could bring death to the rider as well as to the horse.

George was undisturbed by any threat of physical danger to himself. The Rockies are haunts of great animals easily aroused to ferocity—grizzly bears, mountain lions, moose, caribou and bighorn sheep—but in his letters George never mentioned encounters with wild beasts, usually the favourite topic of explorers.

Quite casually he wrote to Anna about getting caught alone in a blizzard high up on the face of a mountain peak.

121

After getting back to the lake, we took a run up into the mountains, chiefly for the purpose of procuring alpine plants which are now in their perfection of spring beauty. Camped the first night in a dense grove of spruce with a roaring fire, luxury unknown to the plains. Took horses to summit of pass next morning and then separated. It was a blustery morning but I got a couple of photos which I hope may turn out well. Climbed up to the peak about 1,000 feet above the pass, from which a perfect panorama of snowy peaks in all directions. The wind was blowing madly . . . . Took a lot of bearings and made a sketch of neighbouring mountains, then came down again collecting plants en route. The front of the mountain I was on ended in a nearly sheer cliff of about 1,000 feet or more, with a green valley with a little lake surrounded by patches of old snowdrifts at the bottom, forming source of one branch of the brook in the pass. Without warning, great snow flurries came from beyond the pines, whirling excitedly in all directions, but chiefly in my eyes . . . . I squatted in the most sheltered nook possible and proceeded to press plants for an hour or more. About 5 p.m. snow abated except on mountain-tops . . . . Horses looked miserable tied up to trees scraping about among the stones for blades of grass, as glad as ourselves to start back to camp on lower level, where snow turned to rain.

After every expedition Dawson returned to Ottawa and wrote a comprehensive report. His combination of energies, talents and achievements earned for him a great deal of fame and the job of assistant director of the Geological Survey of Canada. The title was fine and impressive but the job meant long irksome winters in Ottawa which were very hard. The fame, however, brought the occasional unexpected reward. Mail came to him from all over the world, usually dealing with geological matters, but a letter from France (undated) made him laugh aloud. It was from his old friend Rimmer, who had crossed the Atlantic with him in the *Lake Erie* in 1869.

Dear Dawson:
    You will wonder who in the world is writing to you from Cannes . . .? What a long time it is since we sailed the briny deep fishing for Endosmodes! You will remember that you left me at Crewe Works learning the noble art of becoming an English mechanic . . . Xmas of 1872 I went up to London for a holiday and thought to give you a surprise. On 26 December, after a long walk, I arrived at your diggings on Halkin Street and learned to my chagrin that you had again sought the Far West . . . some time later I received from a chum a paper which contained some valuable information about some discovery you had made in the far west, I regret to say I have quite forgotten what it was either perhaps an Endosmode of gigantic proportions or an entombed mammoth . . .? Well, it struck me that I might as well offer you some congratulations, and although I had not your address, I thought that any boor of a postmaster would know the address of a fellow who had discovered a mammoth, and accordingly address you—
    Geologist!!! Late of London—Montreal.

123

Good old Rimmer! He was as vague as ever about scientific matters, but he was right in one thing. The postmaster had forwarded the letter immediately to Dr. Dawson in Ottawa.

It seemed everyone in Canada knew George by this time. His fame threatened to take over his life. He was "a renowned popular lecturer, conversationalist, clubman and travelling companion," says A. H. Lang. "Westerners not connected with mining used his maps and reports, and spoke with pride of having seen or met him. . . . At least forty years after his death he had a legendary reputation, particularly among older prospectors, who avidly consulted his reports in libraries or by other means, realizing that nothing could be as infallible and up-to-date as they thought the reports were."

Every winter he spent in Ottawa, George became more depressed and suffered more from recurrences of his old headaches. But he was still Skookum Tumtum, who put on a brave, cheery face for the world. He was a popular member of the fashionable Rideau Club where, dining at tables covered with white damask linen and set with crystal and sterling silver, he held listeners enthralled with his tales of the north, or sent them into gales of laughter with his quips. Yet in his heart he preferred the campfire, a grilled trout he had caught himself, and the natural wisdom and quiet companionship of another woodsman.

12
Fame

The summer with Rankine on the Queen Charlotte Islands was the last George spent in close association with any member of his family. As the years passed and his fame spread, he had less and less time in Montreal. He always planned to be home for Christmas, but sometimes couldn't manage it. Most of all he enjoyed Anna's children (she eventually had a family of nine). As adults they remembered the Christmases when Uncle George came—an elf-like Santa Clause who arrived at their door with the jingling of sleigh bells, bringing great bundles of gifts and filling their home with fun and laughter.

George's parents were getting old. In 1884, his father was still principal of McGill—and of McGill Normal School which he had helped found. That year he was knighted by Queen Victoria for his great contribution to Canadian education and geology. Eva was now married and living in England. Rankine had become a ship's doctor and was always somewhere on the high seas. William, who had graduated at the top of his class in engineering in Paris, was quietly becoming famous on his own—as a bridge-builder, as an engineed with the Canadian Pacific Railway, and finally as a pioneer in the work of charting tides and currents in the North Atlantic.

George wished them well—mostly through letters to Anna—but was, himself always off on a new adventure.

He had discovered the Yukon. While the Rockies had aroused in him the passion of first love, the Yukon was to him by far the most beautiful part of Canada. He shared this love with his friend William Ogilvie, a surveyor employed by the Department of the Interior.

The two were concerned with boundaries. The line between Alaska and Canada had never been actually marked and the area had never been properly surveyed or mapped, although it was known to be a gold-bearing region. Miners were already panning along some of the rivers when Dawson and Ogilvie made their first explorations in 1887.

While it was Ogilvie who had been commissioned to mark the boundary between Canada and the United States, it was George who was to travel into wild, remote country to drive a wooden post to mark the corner of the eastern border between British Columbia and the Yukon.

Ogilvie and Dawson set out together from Ottawa on the 22 April, and travelled by Canadian Pacific Railway to Victoria. They arrived at Wrangell at the mouth of the Stikine River in early May, and, on the 18th, went up the river by the first steamer of the season, to Telegraph Creek, the head of navigation. From there they travelled by pack animal to Dease Lake in northern British Columbia, arriving on 5 June, only to find that the lake was still filled with ice. Three men had been sent on ahead to build boats, and all was ready to go. So it was frustrating to have to wait for the ice to break up.

126

And then a more serious difficulty arose. George wanted to go into Frances Lake, to explore and map the area, but nearly all the local Indians refused to go with him because of the great dangers involved.

"You can hardly conceive the intense horror the men have of going up Frances Lake," George wrote to Anna. They told him of fourteen deaths that had occurred on such journeys, eight of them from drownings. And now the place was haunted by the many spirits of these unhappy souls who wanted others to join them.

Nevertheless George was determined to go on—and so he did—although he admitted that he found "the ascent of the Liard River and Frances Lake unexpectedly difficult and tedious." Three canyons proved impassable, and in one place they had to make a portage of seventy miles.

When they arrived at the Upper Pelly River on the 29 July, they had about a month's provisions left. They had, besides, only their scientific instruments and one small camping outfit. The heavy wooden boats had long since been abandoned and the canoes were worn out. There remained "a canvas cover from which to construct a canoe." Here the Indian guides were paid off, and to their great delight were permitted to turn back. During this journey, for more than six weeks, from Lower Post to the confluence of the Pelly and Lewes rivers, they had met no other human being.

Eventually Ogilvie was left at the Alaskan border to establish his first observation post, where he was to spend the winter, while George returned by way of Chilkoot and thence to the coast. He figured that he had travelled about 1,322 miles that summer—an eventful and marvellous trip—

but especially memorable to George and his friend William Ogilvie for one special moment they shared.

It had occurred when they were drifting one evening on the clear waters of a snow-fed lake. Brilliant orange and red fireweed jewelled the shoreline and spread back in a carpet across the valley until the colours darkened and blended into the deep purple of rolling foothills. Behind the hills rose the great white-capped peaks of the Yukon Coast Range, dramatically etched against the cloudless blue sky. The warm, fragrant stillness of the late afternoon was broken only by the occasional cry of a nesting water-fowl.

Ogilvie spoke softly. "I know what you're thinking, Dawson. Gold."

George smiled.

"There's gold in the Yukon, Ogilvie, and one day some-one's going to strike it rich, and then there'll be one of the biggest rushes the world has ever seen. Not on the Forty-mile, where the prospectors are panning now, but along the Klondike River—somewhere."

Ogilvie was silent for a few moments, watching a caribou break through the tall fireweed and lower its stately head to drink from the mirrored surface of the lake.

"If you're so sure you know where gold is to be found, why don't you turn prospector and get rich, Dawson?"

George frowned and then his eyes twinkled.

"Once, when I was a small boy, a playmate of mine—a fellow named O'Hara—asked me what I would do if I struck it rich. I didn't know then, and I still don't. I'm always hap-piest in the wilderness, where everything I need can be packed into a canoe."

He paused to point at a black duck and her brood of fluffy ducklings which came sailing smoothly out of the sedges. The canoe drifted silently.

For the next three seasons George Dawson returned to the Yukon. Each year he went back with increasing reluctance to Ottawa where, as assistant director of the Geological Survey, his desk was always piled high with paperwork which had to be done.

And then in 1891 he had to give up his Yukon expedition. He was asked to perform a new and very different duty.

War had almost broken out between Canada and the United States after the seizure of several Canadian ships hunting for seals in the Bering Sea.

The Pribilof Islands off the coast of Alaska, the only breeding ground of the fur seals, had been purchased by the United States from Russia in 1867, and after that the United States had claimed a monopoly on the seals, not only on the islands, but also in the open sea. Canada would not recognize the U.S. claim. Finally it was agreed that each country should present its case before a neutral board of international arbitration in Paris. Dr. George Dawson was asked to represent Canada. With Sir George Baden-Powell from Great Britain, he set out to investigate. The two men cruised north in a chartered steamer to the bare and lonely Pribilof Islands, and then criss-crossed the North Pacific, back and forth, making observations. Sir Baden-Powell wrote of this experience, "Altogether our cruise occupied nearly nine months, during which time, according to the log, we travelled some 9,000 miles, mostly in fog, gales, and very invigorating cold."

George was more concerned about the seals themselves. As he watched them in their natural habitat, he must have regretted that men were willing to destroy such beautiful animals just to provide themselves with luxury. He wrote a poem.

> Strong and alone you swim, and far
> Amid the spume of cold blue seas
> That beat across the bar
> Against the ebbing tide. The breeze
> Blows darkly up the island strait
> Between the silent ranks of trees
> That hear you roar and stand and wait . . . .

But he was caught in the net of the society in which he lived. It was a society that gave no thought to the question of hunting. Seals were meat and fur for people and that was all there was to it. The only question was, to whom did the bounty belong? George's job was to determine that.

Together the two men prepared their case. In February they went to Washington, and in May to London. Here George was so warmly welcomed and received so many invitations from people that he found it hard to find time to do his work. In March of 1893 he went to Paris, where he followed proceedings of the arbitration with the keenest interest. By September of that year he was back in Ottawa, anxiously awaiting news of the outcome.

Word came at last that the dispute had been settled—in favour of Canada. For his part in the investigations, for his masterful reports, and for the successful presentation of the matter, George was made a Companion of the Order of St. Michael and St. George by Queen Victoria.

In the course of his career he received many other honours, including the degree of Doctor of Science from Princeton in 1877, and that of Ll.D from Queen's University, Kingston, in 1890, from McGill in 1891, and from the University of Toronto some years later. In 1891 he was awarded the Bigsby Gold Medal by the Geological Society for his services in the cause of geology, and was also elected a Fellow of the Royal Society. Two years later he was elected president of the Royal Society of Canada, and in 1897 was president of the geological section of the British Association for the Advancement of Science. The same year he was awarded the Gold Medal of the Royal Geological Society, and became the president of the Geological Society of America.

In 1895 Dr. George Dawson was appointed head of the Geological Survey in Canada. He had reached the top.

George Dawson was not in the Yukon when, in 1896, George Carmack and Robert Henderson discovered gold on creeks flowing into the Klondike River, thereby touching off one of the greatest gold rushes the world has ever known. He was never in the Yukon during those boom days, but the name Klondike Dawson was a name on everyone's tongue. In Ottawa his office was mobbed by would-be prospectors and miners, because he was the one who had explored and mapped all of the Yukon, and he had indicated on his geological maps where gold would most likely be found. These maps—the only ones of their kind—were worth more than if they had been sheets of pure gold. If he had been the least bit greedy or unscrupulous, George could have sold his maps and the advice he gave so freely. He could have become a rich man without moving from behind his desk. In fact, however, he didn't make a cent out of the Klondike Gold Rush.

William Ogilvie was in the Yukon when the first miners struck it rich. He was busy surveying when Jacques Ladue, an enterprising French Canadian, planned a boom town, and began selling housing lots with more speed than care. Ogilvie was, in fact, the only civil servant in the area when trouble and violence threatened to break out because of overlapping boundaries of the staked claims. As honest and incorruptible as Dawson, he was immune to gold fever. When he surveyed a line, no one questioned it. A miner named Jim White found that his claim, after Ogilvie had surveyed it, was only three inches wide. He may have grumbled but he did not dispute it. He was nicknamed ever afterwards Three-Inch-White.

Soon building lots in the boom town were being as hotly contested as claims in the gold fields. In desperation, Jacques Ladue sent for Ogilvie and asked if he would survey the town lots and settle disputes before there was bloodshed. He was willing to pay whatever Ogilvie asked.

Ogilvie gave his answer at once.

"I'm a civil servant and receive my salary from the Canadian government," he said. "I'll survey the lots for you, because it's my duty to do whatever I can to keep the peace, but I can't accept money."

He thought for a moment, and then added suddenly, "I would like to ask one favour in return."

"What's that?"

"I'd like to name your city after a friend—the finest man I've ever known."

Dawson City

"Fair enough," said Jacques Ladue.

That night William Ogilvie wrote a letter to Ottawa. It was addressed to Dr. George Dawson. Weeks later George read the letter, and his blue eyes twinkled with pleasure. He pulled out one of his maps of the Yukon, made a dot, and wrote in a new name:

Dawson City

George died five years later. On Thursday, 18 February, 1901, he worked all day in his office in Ottawa. That evening he dined as usual at the Rideau Club, but the next morning he was in bed with acute bronchitis. A telegram was sent to his mother, Lady Dawson, in Montreal, and she came at once, arriving in Ottawa on Saturday evening. When she reached her son's room in his apartment at Victoria Chambers, she found that he had died fifteen minutes before. He was in his fifty-second year.

133

The next morning newspapers across the country carried the headlines: CANADA MOURNS HER LOSS.

Every map of Canada bears the name of the Little Doctor—not only Dawson City, but a bay in Manitoba, a mountain and glacier in British Columbia, and the Dawson Range of mountains in Yukon Territory. But perhaps George would be most pleased that he is remembered by a tiny species of mouse, named in his honour, whose descendants still scamper freely across the tundra of the Far North.

BIBLIOGRAPHY

Berton, Pierre, *The Golden Trail*. Toronto, Macmillan, 1954.

Brown, George W., *Building the Canadian Nation*. Toronto, J.M. Dent & Sons, 1966.

Butler, Sir William Francis, *The Great Lone Land*. Toronto, Musson, 1924.

Carr, Emily, *Klee Wyck*. Toronto, Clarke Irwin, 1951.

Collard, Edgar Andrew, *Canadian Yesterdays*. Toronto, Longman, 1955.

Collard, Edgar Andrew, *Montreal Yesterdays*. Toronto, Longman, 1962.

Cowrie, Isaac, *The Company of Adventurers*. Toronto, Wm. Briggs, 1913.

Crabtree, Peter, and others, eds. *The Illustrated Natural History of Canada Series*. Toronto, Jack McClelland, 1970. Copyright Natural Science of Canada Limited.

Dawson, George Mercer, *Extracts from the Report on an Exploration made in 1887 in the Yukon District, N.W.T. and Adjacent Portion of British Columbia*. London, Downey & Company, 1898.

Dawson, George Mercer, *Report on the Geology and Resources of the Region in the Vicinity of the 49th Parallel*. Montreal, Dawson Bros., 1875.

Dawson, James, "Recollections of His Life," edited by Marjory Whitelaw, *Dalhousie Review* (Autumn 1973), Halifax, Dalhousie University.

Dawson, Sir John William, *Fifty Years of Work in Canada*, edited by Rankine Dawson. London, Ballantyne Hanson, 1901.

Dennis, K., *Canoe Trails Through Quetico*. (Quetico Foundation), Toronto, University of Toronto Press, 1959.

Dunbar, Carl Owen, *Historical Geology*. New York, John Wiley and Sons, 1960.

*Early Canada: A Collection of Historical Photographs of the Geo-
logical Survey of Canada,* compiled by E. Hall. Ottawa, Queen's
Printer for the Department of Energy, Mines and Resources, 1967.

Forrester, Marjorie, "Shooting the Stars and Chaining the Land,"
The Beaver (Spring 1960), Winnipeg, Hudson's Bay Company.

Harrington, Bernard J., *Life of Sir William Logan.* Montreal, Dawson
Bros., 1883.

Hinton, Arthur C. and Godsell, Philip H., *The Yukon.* Toronto,
Ryerson, 1954.

Lang, A. H., "Contributions of W. E. Logan and G. M. Dawson to
the Canadian Mineral Industry," *Geological Association of
Canada Proceedings,* Vol. 23, pp. 19-23, Toronto, Geological Association of Canada, 1971.

Lang, A. H., "G. M. Dawson and the Economic Development of
Western Canada," *Canadian Public Administration* (Summer
1971), Vol. 14, pp. 236-55, Toronto, Institute of Public Administration.

Lang, A. H., "Sir William Logan and the Economic Development of
Canada," *Canadian Public Administration,* Vol. 12, No. 4, pp.
551-65, Toronto, Institute of Public Administration, 1969.

Leacock, Stephen, *Canada: The Foundations of Its Future.* Montreal,
The House of Seagram, 1941.

Loudon, W. J., *A Canadian Geologist.* Toronto, Macmillan, 1930.

MacLennan, Hugh, *McGill: The Story of a University.* London,
George Allan & Unwin, 1960.

MacMillan, Cyrus, *McGill and Its Story.* London, John Lane, 1921.

MacPhie, Rev. J. P., *Pictonians at Home and Abroad.* Boston,
Pinkham Press, 1914.

Patterson, Edith, *Tales of Early Manitoba.* Winnipeg, Winnipeg Free
Press, 1967.

Rowan, John J., *The Emigrant Sportsman in Canada.* Toronto, Coles,
1972 (a re-issue of the original published in 1873).

Shaw, Margaret Mason, *Geologists and Prospectors.* Toronto, Clarke
Irwin, 1958.

Spry, Irene M., *The Palliser Expedition:* An Account of John Palliser's British North America Exploring Expedition 1857-1860. Toronto, Macmillan, 1973.

The Nor'Wester (Centennial Edition), Vol. 100, No. 1 (July 15, 1970), Winnipeg, INFO.

Thomas, Henry and Thomas, Dana Lee, *Great Scientists.* Boston, Gordon City Publishing, 1946.

Thomson, Don W., *Men and Meridians:* The History of S arveying and Mapping in Canada, Vol. 2, 1867-1917, Ottawa, Queen's Printer, 1967.

Turner, A. R., "Surveying the International Boundary: The Journal of George M. Dawson," *Saskatchewan History* (Winter 1968) Vol. 21 No. 1, Saskatoon, The Saskatchewan Archives Board of the University of Saskatchewan.

Wallace, Frederick William, *In the Wake of the Windships.* Toronto, Musson, 1927.

Winslow-Spragge, Lois, *Life and Letters of George Mercer Dawson, 1849-1901.* Montreal, 1962. Privately printed.

Wright, James Frederick Church, *Saskatchewan: The History of a Province.* Toronto, McClelland and Stewart, 1955.

INDEX